studysync®

Reading & Writing Companion

Technical Difficulties

studysync

studysync.com

Send all inquiries to:
BookheadEd Learning, LLC
610 Daniel Young Drive
Sonoma, CA 95476

2 3 4 5 6 7 8 9 QSX 20 19 18 17 16 A

Cover, ©iStock.com/DNY59, ©iStock.com/janrysavy, ©iStock.com/alexey_boldin, ©iStock.com/skegbydave

G10U3

STUDENT GUIDE

GETTING STARTED

Welcome to the StudySync Reading and Writing Companion! In this booklet, you will find a collection of readings based on the theme of the unit you are studying. As you work through the readings, you will be asked to answer questions and perform a variety of tasks designed to help you closely analyze and understand each text selection. Read on for an explanation of each section of this booklet.

CORE ELA TEXTS

In each Core ELA Unit you will read texts and text excerpts that share a common theme, despite their different genres, time periods, and authors. Each reading encourages a closer look with questions and a short writing assignment.

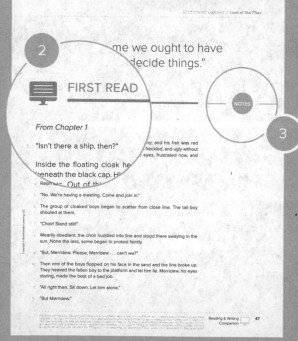

1 INTRODUCTION

An Introduction to each text provides historical context for your reading as well as information about the author. You will also learn about the genre of the excerpt and the year in which it was written.

2 FIRST READ

During your first reading of each excerpt, you should just try to get a general idea of the content and message of the reading. Don't worry if there are parts you don't understand or words that are unfamiliar to you. You'll have an opportunity later to dive deeper into the text.

3 NOTES

Many times, while working through the activities after each text, you will be asked to **annotate** or **make annotations** about what you are reading. This means that you should highlight or underline words in the text and use the "Notes" column to make comments or jot down any questions you may have. You may also want to note any unfamiliar vocabulary words here.

4 · THINK QUESTIONS

These questions will ask you to start thinking critically about the text, asking specific questions about its purpose, and making connections to your prior knowledge and reading experiences. To answer these questions, you should go back to the text and draw upon specific evidence that you find there to support your responses. You will also begin to explore some of the more challenging vocabulary words used in the excerpt.

5 · CLOSE READ & FOCUS QUESTIONS

After you have completed the First Read, you will then be asked to go back and read the excerpt more closely and critically. Before you begin your Close Read, you should read through the Focus Questions to get an idea of the concepts you will want to focus on during your second reading. You should work through the Focus Questions by making annotations, highlighting important concepts, and writing notes or questions in the "Notes" column. Depending on instructions from your teacher, you may need to respond online or use a separate piece of paper to start expanding on your thoughts and ideas.

6 · WRITING PROMPT

Your study of each excerpt or selection will end with a writing assignment. To complete this assignment, you should use your notes, annotations, and answers to both the Think and Focus Questions. Be sure to read the prompt carefully and address each part of it in your writing assignment.

ENGLISH LANGUAGE DEVELOPMENT TEXTS

The English Language Development texts and activities take a closer look at the language choices that authors make to communicate their ideas. Individual and group activities will help develop your understanding of each text.

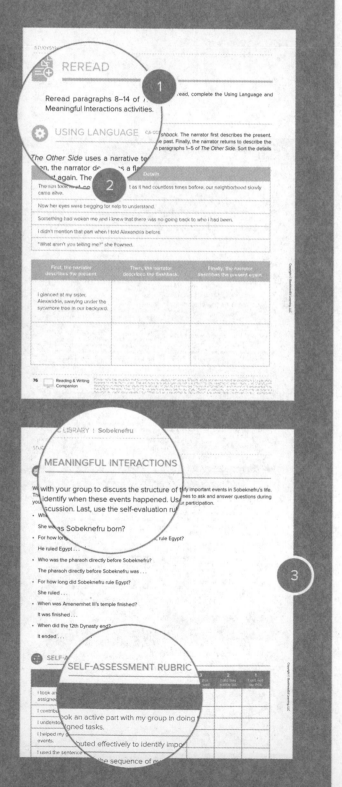

 REREAD

After you have completed the First Read, you will have two additional opportunities to revisit portions of the excerpt more closely. The directions for each reread will specify which paragraphs or sections you should focus on.

 USING LANGUAGE

These questions will ask you to analyze the author's use of language and conventions in the text. You may be asked to write in sentence frames, fill in a chart, or you may simply choose between multiple-choice options. To answer these questions, you should read the exercise carefully and go back in the text as necessary to accurately complete the activity.

 MEANINGFUL INTERACTIONS & SELF-ASSESSMENT RUBRIC

After each reading, you will participate in a group activity or discussion with your peers. You may be provided speaking frames to guide your discussions or writing frames to support your group work. To complete these activities, you should revisit the excerpt for textual evidence and support. When you finish, use the Self-Assessment Rubric to evaluate how well you participated and collaborated.

EXTENDED WRITING PROJECT

The Extended Writing Project is your opportunity to explore the theme of each unit in a longer written work. You will draw information from your readings, research, and own life experiences to complete the assignment.

1 WRITING PROJECT

After you have read all of the unit text selections, you will move on to a writing project. Each project will guide you through the process of writing an argumentative, narrative, informative, or literary analysis essay. Student models and graphic organizers will provide guidance and help you organize your thoughts as you plan and write your essay. Throughout the project, you will also study and work on specific writing skills to help you develop different portions of your writing.

2 WRITING PROCESS STEPS

There are five steps in the writing process: **Prewrite**, **Plan**, **Draft**, **Revise**, and **Edit, Proofread, and Publish**. During each step, you will form and shape your writing project so that you can effectively express your ideas. Lessons focus on one step at a time, and you will have the chance to receive feedback from your peers and teacher.

3 WRITING SKILLS

Each Writing Skill lesson focuses on a specific strategy or technique that you will use during your writing project. The lessons begin by analyzing a student model or mentor text, and give you a chance to learn and practice the skill on its own. Then, you will have the opportunity to apply each new skill to improve the writing in your own project.

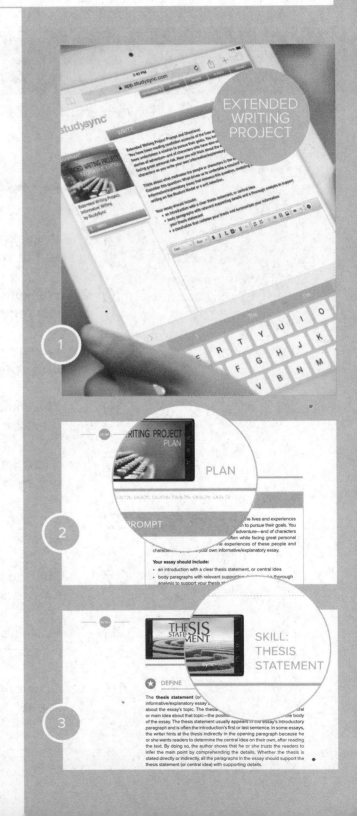

Technical Difficulties

TEXTS

ENGLISH LANGUAGE DEVELOPMENT TEXTS

EXTENDED WRITING PROJECT

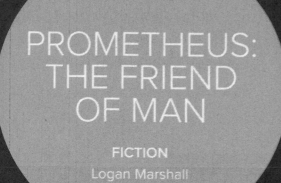

PROMETHEUS: THE FRIEND OF MAN

FICTION
Logan Marshall
1914

INTRODUCTION

Ancient Greeks and other cultures developed myths and legends to explain the origins of their gods, heroes and practices, as well as the laws of nature. These dramatic and often tragic narratives offer insight into the political, religious, and social structures in place at the time. The selection here from author Logan Marshall's collection of myths and legends tells the story of Prometheus, the Titan who defies Jupiter's command and provides fire to humans. Although motivated by a desire to promote progress and prosperity, Prometheus is severely punished by the gods for his act.

"And from your race shall spring the hero who will break my chains and set me free."

FIRST READ

1 Many, many centuries ago there lived two brothers, Prometheus or Forethought, and Epimetheus or Afterthought. They were the sons of those Titans who had fought against Jupiter and been sent in chains to the great prison-house of the lower world, but for some reason had escaped punishment.

2 Prometheus, however, did not care for **idle** life among the gods on Mount Olympus. Instead he preferred to spend his time on the earth, helping men to find easier and better ways of living. For the children of earth were not happy as they had been in the golden days when Saturn ruled. Indeed, they were very poor and wretched and cold, without fire, without food, and with no shelter but miserable caves.

3 "With fire they could at least warm their bodies and cook their food," Prometheus thought, "and later they could make tools and build houses for themselves and enjoy some of the comforts of the gods."

4 So Prometheus went to Jupiter and asked that he might be permitted to carry fire to the earth. But Jupiter shook his head in wrath.

5 "Fire, indeed!" he exclaimed. "If men had fire they would soon be as strong and wise as we who dwell on Olympus. Never will I give my **consent**."

6 Prometheus made no reply, but he didn't give up his idea of helping men. "Some other way must be found," he thought.

7 Then, one day, as he was walking among some reeds he broke off one, and seeing that its hollow stalk was filled with a dry, soft pith, exclaimed:

8 "At last! In this I can carry fire, and the children of men shall have the great gift in spite of Jupiter."

NOTES

9   Immediately, taking a long stalk in his hands, he set out for the dwelling of the sun in the far east. He reached there in the early morning, just as Apollo's chariot was about to begin its journey across the sky. Lighting his reed, he hurried back, carefully guarding the precious spark that was hidden in the hollow stalk.

10 Then he showed men how to build fires for themselves, and it was not long before they began to do all the wonderful things of which Prometheus had dreamed. They learned to cook and to **domesticate** animals and to till the fields and to mine precious metals and melt them into tools and weapons. And they came out of their dark and gloomy caves and built for themselves beautiful houses of wood and stone. And instead of being sad and unhappy they began to laugh and sing. "Behold, the Age of Gold has come again," they said.

11 But Jupiter was not so happy. He saw that men were gaining daily greater power, and their very prosperity made him angry.

12 "That young Titan!" he cried out, when he heard what Prometheus had done. "I will punish him."

13 But before punishing Prometheus he decided to vex the children of men. So he gave a lump of clay to his blacksmith, Vulcan, and told him to mold it in the form of a woman. When the work was done he carried it to Olympus.

14 Jupiter called the other gods together, bidding them give her each a gift. One bestowed upon her beauty, another, kindness, another, skill, another, curiosity, and so on. Jupiter himself gave her the gift of life, and they named her Pandora, which means "all-gifted."

15 Then Mercury, the messenger of the gods, took Pandora and led her down the mountain side to the place where Prometheus and his brother were living.

16 "Epimetheus, here is a beautiful woman that Jupiter has sent to be your wife," he said.

17 Epimetheus was delighted and soon loved Pandora very deeply, because of her beauty and her goodness.

18 Now Pandora had brought with her as a gift from Jupiter a golden casket. Athena had warned her never to open the box, but she could not help wondering and wondering what it contained. Perhaps it held beautiful jewels. Why should they go to waste?

19   At last she could not contain her curiosity any longer. She opened the box just a little to take a peep inside. Immediately there was a buzzing, whirring sound, and before she could snap down the lid ten thousand ugly little creatures had jumped out. They were diseases and troubles, and very glad they were to be free.

20   All over the earth they flew, entering into every household, and carrying sorrow and distress wherever they went.

21   How Jupiter must have laughed when he saw the result of Pandora's curiosity!

22   Soon after this the god decided that it was time to punish Prometheus. He called Strength and Force and bade them seize the Titan and carry him to the highest peak of the Caucasus Mountains. Then he sent Vulcan to bind him with iron chains, making arms and feet fast to the rocks. Vulcan was sorry for Prometheus, but dared not disobey.

23   So the friend of man lay, miserably bound, naked to the winds, while the storms beat about him and an eagle tore at his liver with its cruel talons. But Prometheus did not utter a groan in spite of all his sufferings. Year after year he lay in agony, and yet he would not complain, beg for mercy or repent of what he had done. Men were sorry for him, but could do nothing.

24   Then one day a beautiful white cow passed over the mountain, and stopped to look at Prometheus with sad eyes.

25   "I know you," Prometheus said. "You are Io, once a fair and happy maiden dwelling in Argos, doomed by Jupiter and his jealous queen to wander over the earth in this **guise**. Go southward and then west until you come to the great river Nile. There you shall again become a maiden, fairer than ever before, and shall marry the king of that country. And from your race shall spring the hero who will break my chains and set me free."

26   Centuries passed and then a great hero, Hercules, came to the Caucasus Mountains. He climbed the rugged peak, slew the fierce eagle, and with mighty blows broke the chains that bound the friend of man.

Please note that excerpts and passages in the StudySync® library and this workbook are intended as touchstones to generate interest in an author's work. The excerpts and passages do not substitute for the reading of entire texts, and StudySync® strongly recommends that students seek out and purchase the whole literary or informational work in order to experience it as the author intended. Links to online resellers are available in our digital library. In addition, complete works may be ordered through an authorized reseller by filling out and returning to StudySync® the order form enclosed in this workbook.

Reading & Writing Companion   **7**

THINK QUESTIONS CA-CCSS: CA.RL.9-10.1, CA.RL.9-10.3, CA.RL.9-10.4, CA.L.9-10.4a, CA.L.9-10.4d

1. How does Jupiter respond to Prometheus's request to take fire to the earth and why? What does Jupiter's response show about him? Cite strong textual evidence to support your answer.

2. Who has more power, Jupiter or Prometheus? How do you know? Use evidence from the text to support your answer.

3. What does the story of Prometheus reveal about the gods and their characters? In what ways are the gods both like and unlike typical human beings?

4. Use context to determine the meaning of the word **consent** as it is used in "Prometheus: The Friend of Man." Write your definition of "consent" here and explain the basis for your definition. Then look "consent" up in a dictionary and compare your definition with the one in the dictionary. How accurate was your initial definition?

5. Use context to determine the meaning of the word **vex** as it is used in "Prometheus: The Friend of Man." Write your definition of "vex" here and explain the basis for your definition. Verify your preliminary definition by checking it in context and then in a dictionary.

CLOSE READ

CA-CCSS: CA.RL.9-10.1, CA.RL.9-10.3, CA.RL.9-10.2, CA.RL.9-10.7, CA.W.9-10.5, CA.W.9-10.9a

Reread the excerpt from "Prometheus: The Friend of Man." As you reread, complete the Focus Questions below. Then use your answers and annotations from the questions to help you complete the Writing Prompt.

 FOCUS QUESTIONS

1. In what different ways does the text distinguish Prometheus's character from that of the other gods on Mount Olympus?

2. The third paragraph describes Prometheus's intent in helping man. How does he expect to improve life for man and help him live a better life? What do his goals for man reveal about his perception of the relationship between the gods and men?

3. Why do you think Prometheus is punished so severely for his actions? How does Prometheus respond to his punishment, and what does this response reveal about his character?

4. What different, perhaps conflicting messages does the Prometheus myth convey about challenging the authority of the gods?

5. According to Greek legend, Prometheus created men from mud. Then, as this story makes clear, he gave them the gift of fire. To what extent can Prometheus's act of giving men fire be considered another act of creation? What responsibility does he assume when he gives men the gift of fire?

WRITING PROMPT

Find an image online of the painting *Prometheus Bound* by Peter Paul Rubens. Write a response in which you compare and contrast the representation of the Prometheus myth in the text and in the painting. In your response, discuss what is emphasized and absent in each treatment. How does the painting contribute to your understanding of Prometheus's character and the themes that are developed through it?

Please note that excerpts and passages in the StudySync® library and this workbook are intended as touchstones to generate interest in an author's work. The excerpts and passages do not substitute for the reading of entire texts, and StudySync® strongly recommends that students seek out and purchase the whole literary or informational work in order to experience it as the author intended. Links to online resellers are available in our digital library. In addition, complete works may be ordered through an authorized reseller by filling out and returning to StudySync® the order form enclosed in this workbook.

Reading & Writing Companion   **9**

FRANKENSTEIN

FICTION
Mary Shelley
1818

INTRODUCTION

Mary Shelley began *Frankenstein* as a teenager, part of a competition among her friends to write the best horror story. First published in 1818, this gothic tale of scientific experimentation gone wrong is now considered one of the earliest examples of science fiction. Her character, Dr. Frankenstein, has discovered a way to re-animate dead tissue using an electrical current. His experiment is a success, but the result is a monster brought to life. Horrified by the creature he has created, the doctor flees. Alone and confused, the monster accidentally kills Dr. Frankenstein's younger brother and then murders his best friend. In the excerpt below, the creature explains his actions.

"Life, although it may only be an accumulation of anguish, is dear to me, and I will defend it."

FIRST READ

Excerpt from Chapter 5

1. It was on a dreary night of November that I beheld the accomplishment of my toils. With an anxiety that almost amounted to agony, I collected the instruments of life around me, that I might **infuse** a spark of being into the lifeless thing that lay at my feet. It was already one in the morning; the rain pattered dismally against the panes, and my candle was nearly burnt out, when, by the glimmer of the half-extinguished light, I saw the dull yellow eye of the creature open; it breathed hard, and a convulsive motion agitated its limbs.

2. How can I describe my emotions at this catastrophe, or how delineate the wretch whom with such infinite pains and care I had endeavoured to form? His limbs were in proportion, and I had selected his features as beautiful. Beautiful! Great God! His yellow skin scarcely covered the work of muscles and arteries beneath; his hair was of a lustrous black, and flowing; his teeth of a pearly whiteness; but these luxuriances only formed a more horrid contrast with his watery eyes, that seemed almost of the same colour as the dun-white sockets in which they were set, his shrivelled complexion and straight black lips.

3. The different accidents of life are not so changeable as the feelings of human nature. I had worked hard for nearly two years, for the sole purpose of infusing life into an inanimate body. For this I had deprived myself of rest and health. I had desired it with an ardour that far exceeded moderation; but now that I had finished, the beauty of the dream vanished, and breathless horror and disgust filled my heart. Unable to endure the aspect of the being I had created, I rushed out of the room and continued a long time traversing my bed-chamber, unable to compose my mind to sleep. At length lassitude succeeded to the tumult I had before endured, and I threw myself on the bed in my clothes, endeavouring to seek a few moments of forgetfulness. But it was in vain; I slept, indeed, but I was disturbed by the wildest dreams. I thought I saw Elizabeth, in the bloom of health, walking in the streets of Ingolstadt. Delighted

Please note that excerpts and passages in the StudySync® library and this workbook are intended as touchstones to generate interest in an author's work. The excerpts and passages do not substitute for the reading of entire texts, and StudySync® strongly recommends that students seek out and purchase the whole literary or informational work in order to experience it as the author intended. Links to online resellers are available in our digital library. In addition, complete works may be ordered through an authorized reseller by filling out and returning to StudySync® the order form enclosed in this workbook.

Reading & Writing Companion   **11**

and surprised, I embraced her, but as I imprinted the first kiss on her lips, they became livid with the hue of death; her features appeared to change, and I thought that I held the corpse of my dead mother in my arms; a shroud enveloped her form, and I saw the grave-worms crawling in the folds of the flannel. I started from my sleep with horror; a cold dew covered my forehead, my teeth chattered, and every limb became convulsed; when, by the dim and yellow light of the moon, as it forced its way through the window shutters, I beheld the wretch—the miserable monster whom I had created. He held up the curtain of the bed; and his eyes, if eyes they may be called, were fixed on me. His jaws opened, and he muttered some inarticulate sounds, while a grin wrinkled his cheeks. He might have spoken, but I did not hear; one hand was stretched out, seemingly to detain me, but I escaped and rushed downstairs. I took refuge in the courtyard belonging to the house which I inhabited, where I remained during the rest of the night, walking up and down in the greatest agitation, listening attentively, catching and fearing each sound as if it were to announce the approach of the demoniacal corpse to which I had so miserably given life.

Excerpt from Chapter 10

4   ...I suddenly beheld the figure of a man, at some distance, advancing towards me with superhuman speed. He bounded over the crevices in the ice, among which I had walked with caution; his stature, also, as he approached, seemed to exceed that of man. I was troubled; a mist came over my eyes, and I felt a faintness seize me, but I was quickly restored by the cold gale of the mountains. I perceived, as the shape came nearer (sight tremendous and abhorred!) that it was the wretch whom I had created. I trembled with rage and horror, resolving to wait his approach and then close with him in mortal combat. He approached; his **countenance** bespoke bitter anguish, combined with disdain and malignity, while its unearthly ugliness rendered it almost too horrible for human eyes. But I scarcely observed this; rage and hatred had at first deprived me of utterance, and I recovered only to overwhelm him with words expressive of furious detestation and contempt.

5   "Devil," I exclaimed, "do you dare approach me? And do not you fear the fierce vengeance of my arm wreaked on your miserable head? Begone, vile insect! Or rather, stay, that I may trample you to dust! And, oh! That I could, with the extinction of your miserable existence, restore those victims whom you have so diabolically murdered!"

6   "I expected this reception," said the daemon. "All men hate the wretched; how, then, must I be hated, who am miserable beyond all living things! Yet you, my creator, detest and spurn me, thy creature, to whom thou art bound by ties only dissoluble by the annihilation of one of us. You purpose to kill me. How dare you sport thus with life? Do your duty towards me, and I will do

NOTES

mine towards you and the rest of mankind. If you will comply with my conditions, I will leave them and you at peace; but if you refuse, I will glut the maw of death, until it be satiated with the blood of your remaining friends."

7   "Abhorred monster! Fiend that thou art! The tortures of hell are too mild a vengeance for thy crimes. Wretched devil! You reproach me with your creation, come on, then, that I may extinguish the spark which I so negligently bestowed."

8   My rage was without bounds; I sprang on him, impelled by all the feelings which can arm one being against the existence of another.

9   He easily eluded me and said,

10 "Be calm! I entreat you to hear me before you give vent to your hatred on my devoted head. Have I not suffered enough, that you seek to increase my misery? Life, although it may only be an accumulation of anguish, is dear to me, and I will defend it. Remember, thou hast made me more powerful than thyself; my height is superior to thine, my joints more supple. But I will not be tempted to set myself in opposition to thee. I am thy creature, and I will be even mild and docile to my natural lord and king if thou wilt also perform thy part, which thou owest me. Oh, Frankenstein, be not equitable to every other and trample upon me alone, to whom thy justice, and even thy **clemency** and affection, is most due. Remember that I am thy creature; I ought to be thy Adam, but I am rather the fallen angel, whom thou drivest from joy for no misdeed. Everywhere I see bliss, from which I alone am irrevocably excluded. I was benevolent and good; misery made me a fiend. Make me happy, and I shall again be **virtuous**."

 THINK QUESTIONS CA-CCSS: CA.RL.9-10.1, CA.RL.9-10.4, CA.L.9-10.4a, CA.L.9-10.4d

1. What is the setting of the opening scene of this chapter? What details mentioned in the opening paragraph contribute to the overall mood of the scene? Refer to details from the text to support your answer.

2. How do Frankenstein's feelings about his activities change after he brings his creature to life? What does this change reveal about his character? Quote specific textual evidence to support your answer.

3. What does the creature want from Frankenstein? Support your answer with textual evidence.

4. Use context to determine the meaning of the word **countenance** as it is used in *Frankenstein*. Write your definition of "countenance" here and tell how you arrived at this meaning.

5. Use the context clues provided in the passage to determine the meaning of **virtuous**. Write your definition of "virtuous" here and explain how you determined its meaning. Afterward, check your definition against a dictionary definition and explain how accurate it was.

CLOSE READ
CA-CCSS: CA.RL.9-10.1, CA.RL.9-10.2, CA.RL.9-10.3, CA.RL.9-10.4, CA.RL.9-10.7, CA.RL.9-10.9, CA.W.9-10.1a, CA.W.9-10.1b, CA.W.9-10.4, CA.W.9-10.5, CA.W.9-10.6, CA.W.9-10.9a, CA.W.9-10.10

Reread the excerpt from *Frankenstein*. As you reread, complete the Focus Questions below. Then use your answers and annotations from the questions to help you complete the Writing Prompt.

FOCUS QUESTIONS

1. After reviewing details in the second and third paragraphs of Chapter 5, what ideas about "playing god" do you think Shelley might be conveying through the character of Dr. Frankenstein? How does the film version's characterization of the doctor address these ideas in both similar and different ways?

2. What inferences can you make about the significance of Frankenstein's dream in Chapter 5? What might it suggest about the doctor's state of mind? How might it connect to one or more themes explored in the novel?

3. Review the second through fifth paragraphs in the excerpt from Chapter 10. Contrast the characters of Frankenstein and his creature based on their language, tone, and behavior. Who appears to be the more rational being at this point?

4. Both Frankenstein and the creature make Biblical allusions in Chapter 10. How do the Biblical allusions in the text help the reader to understand Dr. Frankenstein's point of view about his creature, the creature's point of view about Dr. Frankenstein, and each one's view of himself?

5. In the final paragraph of the excerpt from Chapter 10, the creature calls on Frankenstein to accept responsibility for bringing him into existence and for turning him into the monster he has become. To what extent do you think Frankenstein is responsible for the creature's actions?

WRITING PROMPT

Recall that the full title of Mary Shelley's famous novel is *Frankenstein; or, the Modern Prometheus*. To what extent do you think Mary Shelley's association of Frankenstein (the doctor who creates new life from dead tissue) with Prometheus (the Titan from Greek mythology who steals fire from the gods to give to man) is appropriate? Consider similarities and differences in their characters, motivations, actions, fates, and impacts in your response, providing evidence from both the text excerpts and the 1931 film clip. Then briefly connect ideas explored in Shelley's Romantic novel with scientific issues under debate in today's world. What scientific endeavor might have the potential to produce "the Modern Frankenstein"? Support your arguments with evidence from the text as well as from your reading and knowledge of current events.

WORSHIP THE SPIRIT OF CRITICISM:
ADDRESS AT THE PASTEUR INSTITUTE

NON-FICTION
Louis Pasteur
1888

INTRODUCTION

Renowned French scientist Louis Pasteur's research into infectious diseases led to longer and healthier lives for countless millions of people. On November 14, 1888, he addressed his colleagues at the opening of the Pasteur Institute in Paris. In an effort to encourage the advancement of science, Pasteur exhorted his peers to "worship the spirit of criticism" by questioning their own findings. Pasteur's speech also helped define the relationship between science and society as he pressed future generations of scientists to seek "new means of delivering man from the scourges which beset him."

"What I am now asking you, and you will ask of your pupils later on, is what is most difficult to an inventor."

FIRST READ

1   It is now finished, this great building, of which it might be said that there is not a stone but what is the material sign of a generous thought. All the virtues have subscribed to build this dwelling place for work.

2   Alas! mine is the bitter grief that I enter it, a man "vanquished by time," deprived of my masters, even of my companions in the struggle, Dumas, Bouley, Paul Bert, and lastly Vulpian, who, after having been with you, my dear Grancher, my counselor at the very first, became the most energetic, the most convinced champion of this method.

3   However, if I have the sorrow of thinking that they are no more, after having valiantly taken their part in discussions which I have never provoked but I have had to endure; if they cannot hear me proclaim all that I owe to their counsels and support; if I feel their absence as deeply as on the morrow of their death, I have at least the **consolation** of believing that all we struggled for together will not perish. The **collaborators** and students who are now here share our scientific faith.... Keep your early enthusiasm, dear collaborators, but let it ever be regulated by rigorous examinations and tests. Never advance anything that cannot be proved in a simple and decisive fashion.

4   Worship the spirit of criticism. If reduced to itself, it is not an awakener of ideas or a stimulant to great things, but, without it, everything is **fallible**; it always has the last word. What I am now asking you, and you will ask of your pupils later on, is what is most difficult to an inventor.

5   It is indeed a hard task, when you believe you have found an important scientific fact and are feverishly anxious to publish it, to constrain yourself for days, weeks, years sometimes, to fight with yourself, to try and ruin your own experiments and only to proclaim your discovery after having exhausted all contrary hypotheses.

6   But when, after so many efforts, you have at last arrived at a certainty, your joy is one of the greatest which can be felt by a human soul, and the thought that you have contributed to the honor of your country renders that joy still deeper.

7   If science has no country, the scientist should have one, and ascribe to it the influence which his works may have in this world…. Two contrary laws seem to be wrestling with each other nowadays; the one, a law of blood and death, ever imagining new means of destruction and forcing nations to be constantly ready for the battlefield—the other, a law of peace, work and health, ever evolving new means of delivering man from the **scourges** which beset him.

8   The one seeks violent conquests; the other, the relief of humanity. The latter places one human life above any victory; while the former would sacrifice hundreds and thousands of lives to the **ambition** of one. The law of which we are the instruments seeks, even in the midst of carnage, to cure the sanguinary ills of the law of war; the treatment inspired by our sanguinary methods may preserve thousands of soldiers. Which of those two laws will ultimately prevail, God alone knows. But we may assert that French science will have tried, by obeying the law of humanity, to extend the frontiers of life.

THINK QUESTIONS   CA-CCSS: CA.RI.9-10.1, CA.RI.9-10.4, CA.L.9-10.4a, CA.L.9-10.4c

1. What people are uppermost in Louis Pasteur's mind at the opening of the Pasteur Institute? What are his feelings towards them? Use evidence from the text to support your answer.

2. Use details from the text to explain what Pasteur advises scientists to do before they proclaim their discoveries.

3. Write two or three sentences explaining the two "contrary laws" that Pasteur sees at work in the world. Support your answer with textual evidence.

4. Use context clues to determine the meaning of the word **consolation** as it is used in Pasteur's speech. Write down the meaning that you inferred, and explain how you determined it. Then, use a dictionary to clarify its precise meaning.

5. Use context clues to determine the meaning of the word **collaborators** as it is used in Pasteur's speech. Write down the meaning that you inferred, and explain how you determined it. Then, use a dictionary to clarify its precise meaning.

Please note that excerpts and passages in the StudySync® library and this workbook are intended as touchstones to generate interest in an author's work. The excerpts and passages do not substitute for the reading of entire texts, and StudySync® strongly recommends that students seek out and purchase the whole literary or informational work in order to experience it as the author intended. Links to online resellers are available in our digital library. In addition, complete works may be ordered through an authorized reseller by filling out and returning to StudySync® the order form enclosed in this workbook.

Reading & Writing Companion   **17**

CLOSE READ
CA-CCSS: CA.RI.9-10.1, CA.RI.9-10.4, CA.L.9-10.4c, CA.L.9-10.5b, CA.W.9-10.1a, CA.W.9-10.1b, CA.W.9-10.4, CA.W.9-10.5, CA.W.9-10.6, CA.W.9-10.9b, CA.W.9-10.10, CA.L.9-10.5b

Reread the excerpt from Pasteur's speech. As you reread, complete the Focus Questions below. Then use your answers and annotations from the questions to help you complete the Writing Prompt.

FOCUS QUESTIONS

1. Identify words in the second and third paragraphs that carry positive connotations. How do these particular word choices help to convey Pasteur's attitude toward his colleagues? How might his attitude help explain his observation in the first paragraph that "all the virtues" have helped build the new institute? Highlight textual evidence and make annotations to explain your ideas.

2. In the fourth paragraph, Pasteur expresses his attitude toward the role of criticism in the scientific process. Summarize this attitude, citing particular words with denotations and connotations that help to reveal it. Highlight textual evidence and make annotations to explain your choices.

3. In the fifth paragraph, what does Pasteur recognize about the process of scientific research? Highlight strong words that help to convey this message. Then, choose one of the words and identify a synonym for it (you may wish to use a thesaurus or other resource). Use the annotation tool to explain how the connotations of this synonym are either similar to or different from the word Pasteur chose, and tell how Pasteur's word choice helps support his ideas.

4. What are the two "contrary laws," or types of human behavior, that Pasteur discusses in the last two paragraphs? Summarize what he means by these laws. How do the connotations of his words in this section help to make the contrast clear? Support your answer with textual evidence and make annotations to explain your answer choices.

5. Consider this speech in conjunction with the Essential Question for this unit. What responsibility does Pasteur seem to think scientists have for what they create? Highlight and annotate details in the last two paragraphs that support your answer.

WRITING PROMPT

From the details in this speech, what do you conclude is Pasteur's general attitude toward the field of science and those who engage in it? What goals does he think science should pursue? Analyze specific word choices that help to convey Pasteur's positions. Explain how the connotations of the words help to build a tone and to emphasize Pasteur's message.

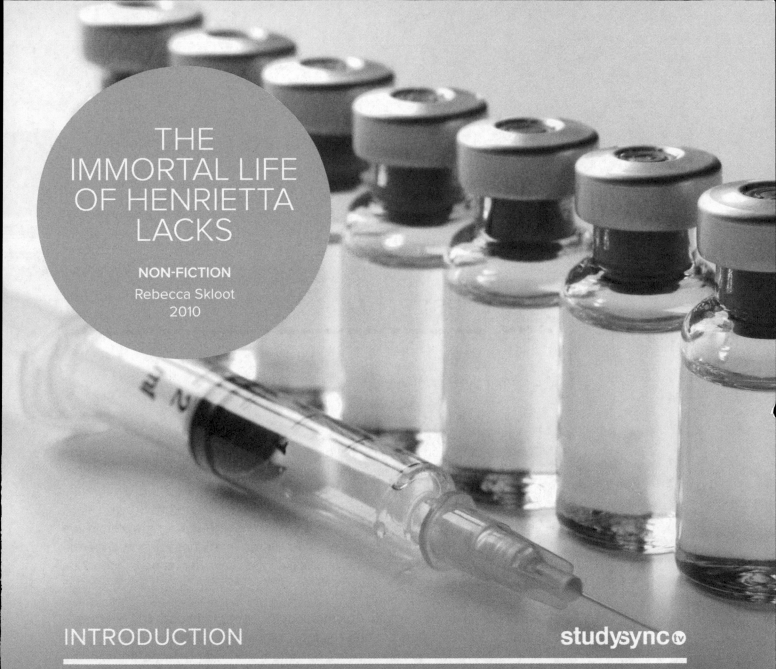

THE IMMORTAL LIFE OF HENRIETTA LACKS

NON-FICTION
Rebecca Skloot
2010

INTRODUCTION

Author Rebecca Skloot was a freshman biology student when she learned of a unique and moving human story. It was a tale of medical discoveries, of ethics, of race, of big business, and of the struggles of an underprivileged family in East Baltimore. Though scientists worldwide know her as HeLa, at the center of this controversy is Henrietta Lacks. She was a poor black tobacco farmer whose cells were removed without her consent as she lay dying of cervical cancer in 1951. The years Skloot spent researching Henrietta exposed the truth—those cells taken from her and kept alive have contributed to great medical breakthroughs including the polio vaccine, cloning, and much more. Yet, Henrietta has remained unknown and her family was never compensated. The world has benefited and many people have profited from Henrietta without even knowing she existed.

"HeLa cells were one of the most important things that happened to medicine in the last hundred years..."

FIRST READ

Excerpt from Prologue

THE WOMAN IN THE PHOTOGRAPH

1   There's a photo on my wall of a woman I've never met, its left corner torn and patched together with tape. She looks straight into the camera and smiles, hands on hips, dress suit neatly pressed, lips painted deep red. It's the late 1940s and she hasn't yet reached the age of thirty. Her light brown skin is smooth, her eyes still young and playful, oblivious to the tumor growing inside her—a tumor that would leave her five children motherless and change the future of medicine. Beneath the photo, a caption says her name is "Henrietta Lacks, Helen Lane or Helen Larson."

2   No one knows who took that picture, but it's appeared hundreds of times in magazines and science textbooks, on blogs and laboratory walls. She's usually identified as Helen Lane, but often she has no name at all. She's simply called HeLa, the code name given to the world's first immortal human *cells—her* cells, cut from her cervix just months before she died.

3   Her real name is Henrietta Lacks.

4   I've spent years staring at that photo, wondering what kind of life she led, what happened to her children, and what she'd think about cells from her cervix living on forever—bought, sold, packaged, and shipped by the trillions to laboratories around the world. I've tried to imagine how she'd feel knowing that her cells went up in the first space missions to see what would happen to human cells in zero gravity, or that they helped with some of the most important advances in medicine: the polio vaccine, chemotherapy, cloning, gene mapping, in vitro fertilization. I'm pretty sure that she—like most of us—

would be shocked to hear that there are trillions more of her cells growing in laboratories now than there ever were in her body.

5   There's no way of knowing exactly how many of Henrietta's cells are alive today. One scientist estimates that if you could pile all HeLa cells ever grown onto a scale, they'd weigh more than 50 million metric tons—an inconceivable number, given that an individual cell weighs almost nothing. Another scientist calculated that if you could lay all HeLa cells ever grown end-to-end, they'd wrap around the Earth at least three times, spanning more than 350 million feet. In her prime, Henrietta herself stood only a bit over five feet tall.

6   I first learned about HeLa cells and the woman behind them in 1988, thirty-seven years after her death, when I was sixteen and sitting in a community college biology class. My instructor, Donald Defler, a gnomish balding man, paced at the front of the lecture hall and flipped on an overhead projector. He pointed to two diagrams that appeared on the wall behind him. They were schematics of the cell reproduction cycle, but to me they just looked like a neon-colored mess of arrows, squares, and circles with words I didn't understand, like "MPF Triggering a Chain Reaction of Protein Activations."

7   I was a kid who'd failed freshman year at the regular public high school because she never showed up. I'd transferred to an alternative school that offered dream studies instead of biology, so I was taking Defler's class for high-school credit, which meant that I was sitting in a college lecture hall at sixteen with words like *mitosis* and *kinase inhibitors* flying around. I was completely lost.

8   "Do we have to memorize everything on those diagrams?" one student yelled.

9   Yes, Defler said, we had to memorize the diagrams, and yes, they'd be on the test, but that didn't matter right then. What he wanted us to understand was that cells are amazing things: There are about one hundred trillion of them in our bodies, each so small that several thousand could fit on the period at the end of this sentence. They make up all our tissues—muscle, bone, blood—which in turn make up our organs.

10   Under the microscope, a cell looks a lot like a fried egg: It has a white (the *cytoplasm*) that's full of water and proteins to keep it fed, and a yolk (the *nucleus*) that holds all the genetic information that makes you *you*. The cytoplasm buzzes like a New York City street. It's crammed full of molecules and vessels endlessly shuttling enzymes and sugars from one part of the cell to another, pumping water, nutrients, and oxygen in and out of the cell. All the while, little cytoplasmic factories work 24/7, cranking out sugars, fats, proteins, and energy to keep the whole thing running and feed the nucleus—the brains of the operation. Inside every nucleus within each cell in your body, there's

an identical copy of your entire genome. That genome tells cells when to grow and divide and makes sure they do their jobs, whether that's controlling your heartbeat or helping your brain understand the words on this page.

11   Defler paced the front of the classroom telling us how mitosis—the process of cell division—makes it possible for embryos to grow into babies, and for our bodies to create new cells for healing wounds or replenishing blood we've lost. It was beautiful, he said, like a perfectly choreographed dance.

12   All it takes is one small mistake anywhere in the division process for cells to start growing out of control, he told us. Just one enzy me misfiring, just one wrong protein activation, and you could have cancer. Mitosis goes haywire, which is how it spreads.

13   "We learned that by studying cancer cells in culture," Defler said. He grinned and spun to face the board, where he wrote two words in enormous print: HENRIETTA LACKS.

14   Henrietta died in 1951 from a vicious case of cervical cancer, he told us. But before she died, a surgeon took samples of her tumor and put them in a petri dish. Scientists had been trying to keep human cells alive in culture for decades, but they all eventually died. Henrietta's were different: they reproduced an entire generation every twenty-four hours, and they never stopped. They became the first immortal human cells ever grown in a laboratory.

15   "Henrietta's cells have now been living outside her body far longer than they ever lived inside it," Defler said. If we went to almost any cell culture lab in the world and opened its freezers, he told us, we'd probably find millions—if not billions—of Henrietta's cells in small vials on ice.

16   Her cells were part of research into the genes that cause cancer and those that suppress it; they helped develop drugs for treating herpes, leukemia, influenza, hemophilia, and Parkinson's disease; and they've been used to study lactose digestion, sexually transmitted diseases, appendicitis, human longevity, mosquito mating, and the negative cellular effects of working in sewers. Their chromosomes and proteins have been studied with such detail and precision that scientists know their every quirk. Like guinea pigs and mice, Henrietta's cells have become the standard laboratory workhorse.

17   "HeLa cells were one of the most important things that happened to medicine in the last hundred years," Defler said.

18   Then, matter-of-factly, almost as an afterthought, he said, "She was a black woman." He erased her name in one fast swipe and blew the chalk from his hands. Class was over.

19 As the other students filed out of the room, I sat thinking, *That's it? That's all we get? There has to be more to the story.*

20 I followed Defler to his office.

21 "Where was she from?" I asked. "Did she know how important her cells were? Did she have any children?"

22 "I wish I could tell you," he said, "but no one knows anything about her."

23 After class, I ran home and threw myself onto my bed with my biology textbook. I looked up "cell culture" in the index, and there she was, a small parenthetical:

24 In culture, cancer cells can go on dividing indefinitely, if they have a continual supply of nutrients, and thus are said to be "immortal." A striking example is a cell line that has been reproducing in culture since 1951. (Cells of this line are called HeLa cells because their original source was a tumor removed from a woman named Henrietta Lacks.)

25 That was it. I looked up HeLa in my parents' encyclopedia, then my dictionary: No Henrietta.

26 As I graduated from high school and worked my way through college toward a biology degree, HeLa cells were omnipresent. I heard about them in histology, neurology, pathology; I used them in experiments on how neighboring cells communicate. But after Mr. Defler, no one mentioned Henrietta.

27 When I got my first computer in the mid-nineties and started using the Internet, I searched for information about her, but found only confused snippets: most sites said her name was Helen Lane; some said she died in the thirties; others said the forties, fifties, or even sixties. Some said ovarian cancer killed her, others said breast or cervical cancer.

28 Eventually I tracked down a few magazine articles about her from the seventies. *Ebony* quoted Henrietta's husband saying, "All I remember is that she had this disease, and right after she died they called me in the office wanting to get my permission to take a sample of some kind. I decided not to let them." *Jet* said the family was angry—angry that Henrietta's cells were being sold for twenty-five dollars a vial, and angry that articles had been published about the cells without their knowledge. It said, "Pounding in the back of their heads was a gnawing feeling that science and the press had taken advantage of them."

NOTES

29   The articles all ran photos of Henrietta's family: her oldest son sitting at his dining room table in Baltimore, looking at a genetics textbook. Her middle son in military uniform, smiling and holding a baby. But one picture stood out more than any other: in it, Henrietta's daughter, Deborah Lacks, is surrounded by family, everyone smiling, arms around each other, eyes bright and excited. Except Deborah. She stands in the foreground looking alone, almost as if someone pasted her into the photo after the fact. She's twenty-six years old and beautiful, with short brown hair and catlike eyes. But those eyes glare at the camera, hard and serious. The caption said the family had found out just a few months earlier that Henrietta's cells were still alive, yet at that point she'd been dead for twenty-five years.

30   All of the stories mentioned that scientists had begun doing research on Henrietta's children, but the Lackses didn't seem to know what that research was for. They said they were being tested to see if they had the cancer that killed Henrietta, but according to the reporters, scientists were studying the Lacks family to learn more about Henrietta's cells. The stories quoted her son Lawrence, who wanted to know if the immortality of his mother's cells meant that he might live forever too. But one member of the family remained voiceless: Henrietta's daughter, Deborah.

31   As I worked my way through graduate school studying writing, I became fixated on the idea of someday telling Henrietta's story. At one point I even called directory assistance in Baltimore looking for Henrietta's husband, David Lacks, but he wasn't listed. I had the idea that I'd write a book that was a biography of both the cells and the woman they came from—someone's daughter, wife, and mother.

32   I couldn't have imagined it then, but that phone call would mark the beginning of a decadelong adventure through scientific laboratories, hospitals, and mental institutions, with a cast of characters that would include Nobel laureates, grocery store clerks, convicted felons, and a professional con artist. While trying to make sense of the history of cell culture and the complicated ethical debate surrounding the use of human tissues in research, I'd be accused of conspiracy and slammed into a wall both physically and metaphorically, and I'd eventually find myself on the receiving end of something that looked a lot like an exorcism. I did eventually meet Deborah, who would turn out to be one of the strongest and most resilient women I'd ever known. We'd form a deep personal bond, and slowly, without realizing it, I'd become a character in her story, and she in mine.

33   Deborah and I came from very different cultures: I grew up white and agnostic in the Pacific Northwest, my roots half New York Jew and half Midwestern Protestant; Deborah was a deeply religious black Christian from the South. I tended to leave the room when religion came up in conversation because it

made me uncomfortable; Deborah's family tended toward preaching, faith healings, and sometimes voodoo. She grew up in a black neighborhood that was one of the poorest and most dangerous in the country; I grew up in a safe, quiet middle-class neighborhood in a predominantly white city and went to high school with a total of two black students. I was a science journalist who referred to all things supernatural as "woo-woo stuff"; Deborah believed Henrietta's spirit lived on in her cells, controlling the life of anyone who crossed its path. Including me.

34 "How else do you explain why your science teacher knew her real name when everyone else called her Helen Lane?" Deborah would say. "She was trying to get your attention." This thinking would apply to everything in my life: when I married while writing this book, it was because Henrietta wanted someone to take care of me while I worked. When I divorced, it was because she'd decided he was getting in the way of the book. When an editor who insisted I take the Lacks family out of the book was injured in a mysterious accident, Deborah said that's what happens when you piss Henrietta off.

35 The Lackses challenged everything I thought I knew about faith, science, journalism, and race. Ultimately, this book is the result. It's not only the story of HeLa cells and Henrietta Lacks, but of Henrietta's family—particularly Deborah—and their lifelong struggle to make peace with the existence of those cells, and the science that made them possible.

 THINK QUESTIONS CA-CCSS: CA.RI.9-10.1, CA.L.9-10.4a, CA.RI.9-10.4

1. According to the author, how do scientists typically refer to Henrietta Lacks? Cite details from the text to support your response.

2. Why does the author begin to research the life of Henrietta Lacks? What does she discover, and why does it make her want to know more? Cite details from the text to support your answer.

3. The author compares and contrasts herself to Deborah Lacks, the daughter of Henrietta. Which differences does she note within the text?

4. Based on the text, what does the word **haywire** mean? Explain which context clues help you arrive at a definition. Then rephrase the sentence in which "haywire" appears.

5. Use context to determine the meaning of the word **chromosomes** as it is used within the text. Write your definition of "chromosomes" here and tell how you found it.

CLOSE READ
CA-CCSS: CA.RI.9-10.1, CA.RI.9-10.2, CA.RI.9-10.3, CA.RI.9-10.4, CA.W.9-10.4, CA.W.9-10.5, CA.W.9-10.6, CA.W.9-10.9b, CA.W.9-10.10

Reread the excerpt from *The Immortal Life of Henrietta Lacks*. As you reread, complete the Focus Questions below. Then use your answers and annotations from the questions to help you complete the Writing Prompt.

 FOCUS QUESTIONS

1. What is the meaning of the term "nucleus" in paragraph 10? What words and phrases in the paragraph help you determine the meaning? Highlight textual evidence and make annotations to help you decode this technical language.

2. Based on the text, what does the term "petri dish" in paragraph 14 mean? What words and phrases in the paragraph help you determine the meaning? Highlight textual evidence and make annotations to help you decode this technical language.

3. Read the paragraphs that describe the information in the articles from *Ebony* and *Jet*. What do the details in these paragraphs add to your understanding of Henrietta Lacks? What might they suggest about science's responsibility for the use of her cells? Highlight textual evidence and make annotations to explain your answer.

4. In the third-to-last paragraph, what contrast does the author draw between herself and Deborah? Why is this contrast important to the story? Highlight textual evidence and make annotations to explain your answer.

5. How does the last paragraph sum up the events that led to the writing of the book? Highlight textual evidence and make annotations to explain your answer.

WRITING PROMPT

What would you want to say to the Lacks family about the contribution to science their mother made through her immortal cells? Write a letter of at least 300 words to Henrietta Lacks' family that tells them. Be sure to include details about the events that occurred after Lacks's cells were preserved. Use outside research and this excerpt to support your ideas.

SILENT SPRING

NON-FICTION
Rachel Carson
1962

INTRODUCTION

I n 1962, scientist and author Rachel Carson published *Silent Spring* as a warning to the public about the environmental risks of pesticides like DDT. Carson's work presented a serious critique of the chemical industry and of the public officials who knowingly condoned the use of harmful chemicals. Immediately, the chemical industry, agricultural organizations, and many government officials questioned the validity of the book's findings. However, scientific studies ordered by President John F. Kennedy found evidence to support Carson's research. These studies spurred an environmental movement across the country, leading to the creation of the Environmental Protection Agency (EPA) in 1970, and a federal ban on DDT two years later.

"Then a strange blight crept over the area and everything began to change."

NOTES

 FIRST READ

From Chapter I: A Fable for Tomorrow

1   There was once a town in the heart of America where all life seemed to live in harmony with its surroundings. The town lay in the midst of a checkerboard of **prosperous** farms, with fields of grain and hillsides of orchards where, in spring, white clouds of bloom drifted above the green fields. In autumn, oak and maple and birch set up a blaze of color that flamed and flickered across a backdrop of pines. Then foxes barked in the hills and deer silently crossed the fields, half hidden in the mists of the fall mornings.

2   Along the roads, laurel, viburnum and alder, great ferns and wildflowers delighted the traveler's eye through much of the year. Even in winter the roadsides were places of beauty, where countless birds came to feed on the berries and on the seed heads of the dried weeds rising above the snow. The countryside was, in fact, famous for the abundance and variety of its bird life, and when the flood of migrants was pouring through in spring and fall people traveled from great distances to observe them. Others came to fish the streams, which flowed clear and cold out of the hills and contained shady pools where trout lay. So it had been from the days many years ago when the first settlers raised their houses, sank their wells, and built their barns.

3   Then a strange **blight** crept over the area and everything began to change. Some evil spell had settled on the community: mysterious maladies swept the flocks of chickens; the cattle and sheep sickened and died. Everywhere was a shadow of death. The farmers spoke of much illness among their families. In the town the doctors had become more and more puzzled by new kinds of sickness appearing among their patients. There had been several sudden and unexplained deaths, not only among adults but even among children, who would be stricken suddenly while at play and die within a few hours.

NOTES

4   There was a strange stillness. The birds, for example—where had they gone? Many people spoke of them, puzzled and disturbed. The feeding stations in the backyards were deserted. The few birds seen anywhere were moribund;they trembled violently and could not fly. It was a spring without voices. On the mornings that had once throbbed with the dawn chorus of robins, catbirds, doves, jays, wrens, and scores of other bird voices there was now no sound; only silence lay over the fields and woods and marsh.

5   On the farms the hens brooded, but no chicks hatched. The farmers complained that they were unable to raise any pigs—the litters were small and the young survived only a few days. The apple trees were coming into bloom but no bees droned among the blossoms, so there was no pollination and there would be no fruit.

6   The roadsides, once so attractive, were now lined with browned and withered vegetations as though swept by fire. These, too, were silent, deserted by all living things. Even the streams were now lifeless. Anglers no longer visited them, for all the fish had died.

7   In the gutters under the eaves and between the shingles of the roofs, a white granular powder still showed a few patches; some weeks before it had fallen like snow upon the roofs and the lawns, the fields and the streams.

8   No witchcraft, no enemy action had silenced the rebirth of new life in this stricken world. The people had done it themselves.

9   This town does not actually exist, but it might easily have a thousand **counterparts** in America or elsewhere in the world. I know of no community that has experienced all the misfortunes I describe. Yet every one of these disasters has actually happened somewhere, and many real communities have already suffered a substantial number of them. A grim specter has crept upon us almost unnoticed, and this imagined tragedy may easily become a stark reality we all shall know.

Excerpted from *Silent Spring* by Rachel Carson, published by Houghton Mifflin Company.

THINK QUESTIONS CA-CCSS: CA.RI.9-10.1, CA.RI.9-10.4, CA.L.9-10.4a, CA.L.9-10.4b

1. Use details from the text to explain what sort of town the author describes in the first two paragraphs. Why does the author describe this town in such detail for readers?

2. What details does the author provide in the fourth through seventh paragraphs to show the impact of the "strange blight" that suddenly descends upon the town? How does her use of these details connect with the fact that she describes them as an "evil spell" that had settled on the community?

3. Why do you think the author waits until the final paragraph to explain that the town she describes does not actually exist? Support your answer with textual evidence.

4. Use context to determine the meaning of the word **counterparts** as it is used in *Silent Spring*. Write your definition of "counterparts" here and tell how you found it.

5. Remembering that the Latin verb "*mori*" means "to die" and the Latin word "*moribundus*" means "dying, at the point of death," use the context clues provided in the passage to determine the meaning of **moribund**. Write your definition of "moribund" here and tell how you got it.

Reading & Writing Companion

CLOSE READ
CA-CCSS: CA.RI.9-10.1, CA.RI.9-10.4, CA.RI.9-10.5, CA.RI.9-10.6, CA.L.9-10.4a, CA.L.9-10.5b, CA.W.9-10.4, CA.W.9-10.5, CA.W.9-10.9b, CA.W.9-10.10

Reread the excerpt from *Silent Spring*. As you reread, complete the Focus Questions below. Then use your answers and annotations from the questions to help you complete the Writing Prompt.

FOCUS QUESTIONS

1. Explain why Rachel Carson wrote this section of her book *Silent Spring* as a fable, considering the fact that the text as a whole is a scientific analysis of how pesticides have entered the food chain and threatened life forms.

2. What does the language in the third paragraph suggest has caused the changes that are taking place in the town? Why do you think Carson uses this kind of language here, and how does it still resemble a fable? Why might Carson have chosen not to identify the specific cause of the blight in the opening chapter of the book, except to say in the second-to-last paragraph that "the people brought it on themselves"?

3. The fourth, fifth, and sixth paragraphs describe the town after the blight. How do the details in this section emphasize the town's state? How do these details help to clarify the meaning of the book's title, *Silent Spring*?

4. In the last sentence, Rachel Carson uses the term "grim specter." What do you think this term means and what words help you understand its meaning? How does the meaning of the word match the point of view she is trying to advance? Discuss how this term also connects to the overall structure of the opening chapter of *Silent Spring*.

5. What does the fictional town described in the opening chapter of *Silent Spring*, representative of many towns all over America, suggest about the responsibility humans have for environmental problems such as those created by the use of pesticides?

WRITING PROMPT

Think of an environmental issue about which you have strong beliefs, such as climate change, use of agricultural hormones, fracking, etc. What actual or potential problems have debates about this issue raised? How has human activity created or contributed to these problems? How might you, like Rachel Carson in the opening chapter of *Silent Spring*, use a fable to introduce your analysis of this issue? Write an introduction to an argument in the form of a fable or some other literary genre designed to alert readers to an environmental problem and capture their attention and interest. Be sure that your introduction uses this fable—or other literary genre—as well as additional informational text structures to illustrate the problem and its effects. Include a moral, or lesson that readers might take away from the experience of reading this introduction. Use your analysis of the chapter from *Silent Spring* as a model.

Please note that excerpts and passages in the StudySync® library and this workbook are intended as touchstones to generate interest in an author's work. The excerpts and passages do not substitute for the reading of entire texts, and StudySync® strongly recommends that students seek out and purchase the whole literary or informational work in order to experience it as the author intended. Links to online resellers are available in our digital library. In addition, complete works may be ordered through an authorized reseller by filling out and returning to StudySync® the order form enclosed in this workbook.

Reading & Writing Companion

31

A CIVIL ACTION

NON-FICTION
Jonathan Harr
1996

INTRODUCTION

When 28 children contracted leukemia in a Massachusetts town, local residents Donna Robbins and Anne Anderson formed a citizen action group and attorney Jan Schlichtmann took the case to court. Jonathan Harr's *A Civil Action* tells the story, including the heavy toll the case took on Schlichtmann. In this excerpt, Anne Anderson gathers information and begins to identify the issues facing the community.

"The water had never tasted right, it never looked right, and it never smelled right."

FIRST READ

Excerpt from Chapter 2

1   Anne thought it strange that three cases of leukemia should occur in the same neighborhood, within a few blocks of each other. She wondered if it was coincidence or if a virus of some sort was circulating. Dr. Truman, she remembered, had mentioned that some cancer researchers suspected a virus might cause childhood leukemia. Although she knew that was an unproven **hypothesis**, she and Carol Gray spent hours speculating about it. ...

2   During a visit to the clinic at Massachusetts General that spring, Anne told Dr. Truman about the Zonas and the Nagles. Wasn't it unusual, she asked, that there were three cases in the same neighborhood?

3   Truman listened in his polite, attentive manner, tall frame slightly stooped, but he would admit later that he did not give Anne's question any serious consideration. He'd learned over the years that parents of children with leukemia tended to develop a heightened awareness of the illness. Everywhere they turned it seemed they encountered a reference to it, or someone else whose child had it. To Truman, this was not an uncommon psychological phenomenon. Many years later, in a deposition, Truman recalled his reaction to Anne's queries: "My response was that on the basis of the number of children with leukemia that I was aware of at the time, and considering the population of the city of Woburn, I did not think the **incidence** of leukemia appeared to be increased. In essence, I dismissed her suggestion."

4   Nor did it occur to Truman a year later, in June 1973, that there was anything unusual about the illness of a two-and-a-half-year-old boy from Woburn named Kevin Kane, Jr. The boy had been referred to Truman from Winchester Hospital where his mother, a nurse, had taken him because of a persistent fever, pallor, and irritability. Two weeks earlier he had been treated unsuccessfully for a respiratory infection that did not respond to penicillin. His

history on presentation at Winchester Hospital included several respiratory infections as well as recurrent episodes of earaches. Winchester referred Kevin Kane to Dr. Truman at Massachusetts General with a "high suspicion" of acute lymphocytic leukemia. Truman confirmed the suspicion. He began treating Kevin Kane on a chemotherapy **regimen** similar to the St. Jude protocol. The child responded well. At four weeks, a bone marrow aspiration revealed that he was in remission.

5 Kevin Kane, Sr., and his wife, Patricia, lived with their four children on Henry Avenue in east Woburn. Henry Avenue curved around the perimeter of a low bluff overlooking the Aberjona marsh. From the back door of the Kane's house, looking east across the expanse of marsh, you could see the houses of the Pine Street neighborhood a quarter of a mile away. If you looked closely, you could see Orange Street and, through the trees, the red-shingled ranch house of the Andersons.

6 Anne found out about the Kane's child from Carol Gray, whose fourteen-year-old son delivered the *Woburn Daily Times* every afternoon along Henry Avenue. In the summer of 1973, as Carol's son made his rounds, he learned that one of the Kane's children had leukemia. He reported the news to his mother, who went immediately to the phone and called Anne. "What the hell is going on here?" Carol said to Anne.

7 With the discovery of yet another leukemia case, Anne began writing down some of her thoughts. She made the first of many lists of the cases she knew about, writing in a spiral notebook the names of the children, their addresses, their ages; and the dates when she figured they had been diagnosed.

8 The **notion** that each case shared some common cause began to obsess her. "The water and the air were the two things we all shared," she said in a deposition some years later. "And the water was bad. I thought there was a virus that might have been transmitted through the water, some kind of a leukemia virus. The water had never tasted right, it never looked right, and it never smelled right. There were times when it was worse than others, usually during the summer, and then it was almost impossible to drink. My mother would bring some water from Somerville to the house on weekends, probably about three quarts, which we used as drinking water. The rest of the time, when we could mask the flavor of it with Zarex or orange juice or coffee or whatever, then we used water from the tap. But you couldn't even mask it. It ruined the dishwasher. The door **corroded** to such a degree that it had to be replaced. The prongs that hold the dishes just gave way and broke off. On a regular basis, the pipes under the kitchen sink would leak, and under the bathroom sink. The faucets had to be replaced. The bathroom faucet dripped constantly. It seemed like no sooner would I get everything fixed and we'd have another problem."

Excerpted from *A Civil Action* by Jonathan Harr, published by Vintage Books.

 THINK QUESTIONS CA-CCSS: CA.RI.9-10.1, CA.RI.9-10.4, CA.L.9-10.4a

1. Refer to one or more details from the text to explain what led Anne to think that local children's leukemia might be caused by a virus in the local environment.

2. Use details from the text to write two or three sentences describing why Dr. Truman rejected Anne's ideas. Support your ideas with textual evidence.

3. Write two or three sentences describing why Anne suspected that the source of the virus might be the neighborhood water supply. Support your answer with textual evidence.

4. Use context to determine the meaning of the word **hypothesis** as it is used in *A Civil Action*. Write your definition of "hypothesis" here and tell how you found it.

5. Use context to determine the meaning of the word **incidence** as it is used in *A Civil Action*. Write your definition of "incidence" here and tell how you found it.

CLOSE READ
CA-CCSS: CA.RI.9-10.1, CA.RI.9-10.2, CA.RI.9-10.3, CA.W.9-10.1a, CA.W.9-10.1b, CA.W.9-10.4, CA.W.9-10.5, CA.W.9-10.6, CA.W.9-10.9b, CA.W.9-10.10

Reread the excerpt from *A Civil Action*. As you reread, complete the Focus Questions below. Then use your answers and annotations from the questions to help you complete the Writing Prompt.

FOCUS QUESTIONS

1. Which key details in paragraph 3 reveal Dr. Truman's experience with the parents of children with leukemia? How does this experience influence his dismissal of Anne's hypothesis about a virus causing leukemia? Highlight evidence from the text and make annotations to support your inferences.

2. In paragraph 4, the text relates that another child in the neighborhood has developed leukemia. Paragraphs 6 and 7 reveal the reactions of Carol and Anne, both mothers of a child with leukemia, to the news. Contrast their actions and attitudes with those of Dr. Truman. Why are they different? Support your answer with textual evidence and make annotations to explain your answer choices.

3. Why is the information in paragraph 5 about the location of the Kane home a key detail? What does it suggest to Anne and Carol? Highlight your textual evidence and make annotations to explain your inferences.

4. In the final paragraph, why does the author focus on Anne's observations about the neighborhood's problems with local water? How does this paragraph support the main idea of the selection? Highlight textual evidence and make annotations to explain your ideas.

5. How does this selection and its central or main idea relate to the Essential Question: "What responsibility do we have for what we create?" Explain what the text suggests about the importance of finding out the truth about the causes of problems such as disease. Highlight text evidence and make annotations to support your explanation.

WRITING PROMPT

Imagine you are Anne. Write a letter to the editor of the local newspaper about the dangers of the local water supply and its possible effect on the health of the children of the community. Have Anne summarize her central ideas about the suspicious nature of the leukemia cases, supporting the ideas with key details. Also have Anne recount the challenges she has faced while trying to get people to pay attention to the problem.

SHADING
THE EARTH

NON-FICTION
Robert Kunzig
2009

INTRODUCTION

studysync

Geoengineering, or the application of science and technology to change the Earth, is currently being proposed as a possible solution to the problem of climate change. With the evidence mounting that the earth's temperature is rising, many believe we should be curbing our fossil fuel dependency and reducing CO2 emissions. Since 2006, improbable ideas such as mirrors in space, whitening clouds, and dropping trees from planes like bombs have moved from the fringes of the scientific community to the mainstream. But have we reached the point where we should seriously consider manipulating our environment on such a large scale? Would doing so be a smart application of manmade technology or an example of science run amok? In "Shading the Earth," an article published in National Geographic in August 2009, Robert Kunzig presents the debate over geoengineering the climate.

"We are already modifying climate by accident..."

 FIRST READ

1   If we don't cut fossil fuels fast enough, global warming may get out of hand. Some scientists say we need a plan B: a giant sunshade that would cool the whole planet.

2   Some call it **hubris**; others call it cool reason. But the idea that we might combat global warming by deliberately engineering a cooler climate—for instance, by constructing some kind of planetary sunshade—has lately migrated from the **fringe** to the scientific mainstream. We are already modifying climate by accident, say **proponents** of geoengineering; why not do something intentional and intelligent to stop it? Hold on, say critics. Global warming shows we understand the Earth too little to engineer it without unintended and possibly disastrous consequences. Both sides worry that facts on the ground—rising seas melting ice, failing crops—may cut short the geoengineering debate. "If a country starts thinking it's in their vital interests to do this, and they have the power, I find it hard to imagine them not doing it," says Ken Caldeira, a climate expert at the Carnegie Institution.

3   Caldeira is talking about the easiest, cheapest form of geoengineering: building a sunshade in the stratosphere out of millions of tons of tiny reflective particles, such as sulfate. Planes, balloons, battleship guns pointed upward—there is no shortage of possible delivery vehicles. And there is little doubt you could cool Earth that way, because volcanoes already do it. After Mount Pinatubo erupted in the Philippines in 1991, launching ten million tons of sulfur into the stratosphere and spreading a sun-dimming haze around the planet, the average temperature dropped by about a degree Fahrenheit for a year. With carefully designed particles, geoengineers might make do with a fraction of that tonnage—though because they fall out of the stratosphere, the particles would have to be delivered continually, year after year. Still, says Caldeira, the sulfate scheme would be "essentially free compared with the other costs of **mitigating** climate change."

NOTES

4   Not so the idea suggested by Roger Angel, an **eminent** astronomer and telescope designer at the University of Arizona. Angel has proposed launching trillions of two-foot-wide, thinner-than- Kleenex disks of silicon nitride—each disk an autonomous robot weighing less than a gram—into space between Earth and the sun, where they could deflect sunlight. By Angel's own reckoning, the scheme would take decades and cost trillions of dollars. With that much time and money, we could wean ourselves from fossil fuels and actually solve the climate problem—by far the better outcome, as Angel and most proponents of geoengineering would agree. Unfortunately, though the recession has temporarily slowed the rise in carbon dioxide emissions, we've made no real progress toward that goal. Some say we're running out of time.

5   If we put up a sunshade without restraining emissions and the sunshade later fails, the climate accident would become a train wreck: The global warming we'd been masking would come rushing at us all at once. That might be the worst unintended consequence of geoengineering, but there could be others—damage to the ozone layer, perhaps, or an increase in drought. If CO2 keeps rising, though, we may face greater emergencies. And what once seemed insane hubris just might become reality.

"Shading the Earth" by Robert J. Kunzig. National Geographic Magazine (August 2009). Used by Permission of National Geographic Creative.

THINK QUESTIONS   CA-CCSS: CA.RI.9-10.1, CA.L.9-10.4a, CA.L.9-10.4c, CA.L.9-10.4b, CA.L.9-10.4d

1. In what ways has the perception of geoengineering changed in recent years and why? Cite evidence from the text in your response.

2. State **three** approaches to addressing the problem of global warming that are either stated or implied in the article. Does the author take a clear position on these? Explain, citing examples from the text in your answer.

3. Based on evidence presented in the third and fourth paragraphs, which do you think is a more plausible solution to the problem of global warming: building a sunshade in the stratosphere from reflective particles or launching disks of silicon nitride into the space between the Earth and the sun? Use text evidence to support your position.

4. Use context to determine the meaning of the word **hubris** as it is used in "Shading the Earth." Write your definition of "hubris" here and tell how you found it. Then use an online or print dictionary to clarify the word's precise meaning.

5. Remembering that the Latin prefix "*pro*" means "for" and the Latin suffix "*-ent*" signifies "someone or something that performs an action," use the context clues provided in the passage to determine the meaning of **proponents**. Write your definition of "proponents" here and tell how you got it. Then use a dictionary and thesaurus to verify your preliminary determination of the meaning of this word.

CLOSE READ
CA-CCSS: CA.RI.9-10.1, CA.RI.9-10.4, CA.RI.9-10.8, CA.SL.9-10.3, CA.L.9-10.4a, CA.L.9-10.4c, CA.L.9-10.6, CA.W.9-10.1a, CA.W.9-10.1b, CA.W.9-10.4, CA.W.9-10.5, CA.W.9-10.6, CA.W.9-10.9b, CA.W.9-10.10

Reread the excerpt from "Shading the Earth." As you reread, complete the Focus Questions below. Then use your answers and annotations from the questions to help you complete the Writing Prompt.

FOCUS QUESTIONS

1. What reasons from supporters of geoengineering does Kunzig present in the second paragraph? What counterclaim, reasons, and evidence from critics of geoengineering does he present afterward? On what point are both sides united, according to Kunzig? How does paragraph 2 alert you to Kunzig's purpose in writing this article?

2. What claim does Kunzig present in the opening of the third paragraph? What evidence does he supply to support this claim? What evidence does he provide to support the claim he presents later that the sunshade would work? How might this evidence be considered fallacious?

3. Select one technical word or phrase from the fourth paragraph and one from the fifth paragraph of "Shading the Earth." Identify the terms' meanings, using context clues and, as necessary, reference materials. What effect do such technical words have on the tone and impact of the article?

4. Paraphrase claims against the sunshade that Kunzig presents in the fifth paragraph. Then quote or paraphrase a counterclaim he presents in response. Does this counterclaim effectively address the issues raised by critics of geoengineering? Use reasons and evidence to support your point of view.

5. Based on the ideas that Kunzig presents in the article, how do you think he would answer this question: "What responsibility do we have for what we create?" Write two or three sentences, using textual evidence to support your response.

WRITING PROMPT

Based on the arguments, claims, and evidence presented in "Shading the Earth" and on your prior knowledge, do you think geoengineering is a good solution to the problem of global warming? Construct a persuasive, well-organized argument in support of your position, using reasons and evidence from the text of "Shading the Earth" to support your claims. You should critically evaluate opposing arguments presented in the article in order to support your own view. Use technical terms where appropriate.

EINSTEIN'S LETTER TO THE PRESIDENT

NON-FICTION
Albert Einstein
1939

INTRODUCTION

In 1933, with the rise of Hitler's Nazi party and its aggression toward Jews, Albert Einstein left Germany and settled in New Jersey, where he took a position as Professor of Theoretical Physics at Princeton University. Lobbied by fellow physicists to use his influence, Einstein sent the following carefully worded letter to President Franklin D. Roosevelt regarding Germany and the development of nuclear weapons.

"Certain aspects of the situation which has arisen seem to call for watchfulness..."

 **FIRST READ**

Albert Einstein
Old Grove Road
Nassau Point
Peconic, Long Island

August 2nd, 1939

F.D. Roosevelt
President of the United States
White House
Washington, D.C.

Sir:

1   Some recent work by E. Fermi and L. Szilard, which has been communicated to me in **manuscript**, leads me to expect that the element uranium may be turned into a new and important source of energy in the immediate future. Certain aspects of the situation which has arisen seem to call for watchfulness and if necessary, quick action on the part of the Administration. I believe therefore that it is my duty to bring to your attention the following facts and recommendations.

2   In the course of the last four months it has been made probable through the work of Joliot in France as well as Fermi and Szilard in America—that it may be possible to set up a nuclear **chain reaction** in a large mass of uranium, by which vast amounts of power and large quantities of new radium-like elements would be generated. Now it appears almost certain that this could be achieved in the immediate future.

NOTES

3   This new phenomenon would also lead to the construction of bombs, and it is **conceivable**—though much less certain—that extremely powerful bombs of this type may thus be constructed. A single bomb of this type, carried by boat and exploded in a port, might very well destroy the whole port together with some of the surrounding territory. However, such bombs might very well prove too heavy for transportion by air.

4   The United States has only very poor ores of uranium in **moderate** quantities. There is some good ore in Canada and former Czechoslovakia, while the most important source of uranium is in the Belgian Congo.

5   In view of this situation you may think it desirable to have some permanent contact maintained between the Administration and the group of physicists working on chain reactions in America. One possible way of achieving this might be for you to **entrust** the task with a person who has your confidence and who could perhaps serve in an unofficial capacity. His task might comprise the following:

6   a) to approach Government Departments, keep them informed of the further development, and put forward recommendations for Government action, giving particular attention to the problem of securing a supply of uranium ore for the United States.

7   b) to speed up the experimental work, which is at present being carried on within the limits of the budgets of University laboratories, by providing funds, if such funds be required, through his contacts with private persons who are willing to make contributions for this cause, and perhaps also by obtaining co-operation of industrial laboratories which have necessary equipment.

8   I understand that Germany has actually stopped the sale of uranium from the Czechoslovakian mines which she has taken over. That she should have taken such early action might perhaps be understood on the ground that the son of the German Under-Secretary of State, von Weizsacker, is attached to the Kaiser-Wilhelm Institute in Berlin, where some of the American work on uranium is now being repeated.

Yours very truly,

Albert Einstein

THINK QUESTIONS   CA-CCSS: CA.RI.9-10.1, CA.RI.9-10.4, CA.L.9-10.4a

1. Refer to one or more details from the text to support your understanding of why Einstein felt that he needed to write this letter to the president.

2. What exactly is the "new phenomenon" Einstein mentions in the second and third paragraphs? Support your answer with textual evidence.

3. What are some of the ways that Einstein suggests the president deal with this information? Support your answer with textual evidence.

4. Use context to determine the meaning of the word **manuscript** as it is used in "Einstein's Letter to the President." Write your definition of "manuscript" here and tell how you found it.

5. Use context to determine the meaning of the word **conceivable** as it is used in "Einstein's Letter to the President." Write your definition of "conceivable" here and tell how you found it.

CLOSE READ

CA-CCSS: CA.RI.9-10.1, CA.RI.9-10.3, CA.RI.9-10.6, CA.W.9-10.2a, CA.W.9-10.2b, CA.W.9-10.4, CA.W.9-10.5, CA.W.9-10.6, CA.W.9-10.9b, CA.W.9-10.10

Reread the excerpt from "Einstein's Letter to the President." As you reread, complete the Focus Questions below. Then use your answers and annotations from the questions to help you complete the Writing Prompt.

FOCUS QUESTIONS

1. Explain how Einstein uses the first paragraph to grab the reader's attention and introduce his purpose. Highlight evidence from the text and make annotations to explain your choices.

2. What is Einstein's point of view about uranium? What ideas or attitudes about uranium does Einstein encourage President Roosevelt to adopt? Highlight evidence from the text and make annotations to explain your choices.

3. In the indented paragraphs, Einstein outlines the responsibilities of a new government official that he is recommending be appointed. What are the responsibilities? Why do you think Einstein gives this information through indented text and bullet points? Highlight evidence from the text and make annotations to support your explanation.

4. What is the significance of the information in the final paragraph? How has Einstein given readers information throughout the letter to prepare them to understand the final paragraph? Highlight evidence from the text and make annotations to support your answer.

5. How is Einstein taking responsibility for the scientific and political situation of his time in this text? Highlight evidence from the text and make annotations to explain your choices.

WRITING PROMPT

Read Albert Einstein's letter to President Roosevelt. Then respond to Einstein in a 300-word memo. In your memo, explain your understanding of Einstein's purpose for writing and point of view. Your response should be written from you, in the present, to Einstein at the time he wrote the letter.

Please note that excerpts and passages in the StudySync® library and this workbook are intended as touchstones to generate interest in an author's work. The excerpts and passages do not substitute for the reading of entire texts, and StudySync® strongly recommends that students seek out and purchase the whole literary or informational work in order to experience it as the author intended. Links to online resellers are available in our digital library. In addition, complete works may be ordered through an authorized reseller by filling out and returning to StudySync® the order form enclosed in this workbook.

Reading & Writing Companion   45

COUNTER-ATTACK

POETRY
Siegfried Sassoon
1918

INTRODUCTION

Siegfried Sassoon was an English soldier, poet, and author who wrote much of his poetry about World War I. Commended for bravery on the Western Front, Sassoon became disillusioned with the conduct of the war, and eventually began speaking out in opposition. As can be seen in "Counter-Attack," his poetry vividly conveys the horrors of trench warfare while sarcastically questioning the motives of those in charge the war effort. Sassoon was a close friend of fellow soldier and poet Wilfred Owen, who was killed in action in 1918.

"O Christ, they're coming at us!"

FIRST READ

1 We'd gained our first **objective** hours before
2 While dawn broke like a face with blinking eyes,
3 Pallid, unshaved and thirsty, blind with smoke.
4 Things seemed all right at first. We held their line,
5 With bombers posted, Lewis guns well placed,
6 And clink of shovels deepening the shallow trench.
7 The place was rotten with dead; green clumsy legs
8 High-booted, sprawled and grovelled along the saps
9 And trunks, face downward, in the sucking mud,
10 Wallowed like trodden sand-bags loosely filled;
11 And naked sodden buttocks, mats of hair,
12 Bulged, clotted heads slept in the plastering slime.
13 And then the rain began,—the jolly old rain!

14 A yawning soldier knelt against the bank,
15 Staring across the morning **blear** with fog;
16 He wondered when the Allemands would get busy;
17 And then, of course, they started with five-nines
18 **Traversing**, sure as fate, and never a dud.
19 Mute in the clamour of shells he watched them burst
20 Spouting dark earth and wire with gusts from hell,
21 While **posturing** giants dissolved in drifts of smoke.
22 He crouched and flinched, dizzy with galloping fear,
23 Sick for escape,—loathing the strangled horror
24 And butchered, frantic gestures of the dead.

25 An officer came blundering down the trench:
26 'Stand-to and man the fire-step! 'On he went...
27 Gasping and bawling, 'Fire- step...counter-attack!'
28 Then the haze lifted. Bombing on the right
29 Down the old sap: machine- guns on the left;

Please note that excerpts and passages in the StudySync® library and this workbook are intended as touchstones to generate interest in an author's work. The excerpts and passages do not substitute for the reading of entire texts, and StudySync® strongly recommends that students seek out and purchase the whole literary or informational work in order to experience it as the author intended. Links to online resellers are available in our digital library. In addition, complete works may be ordered through an authorized reseller by filling out and returning to StudySync® the order form enclosed in this workbook.

Reading & Writing Companion   **47**

30 And stumbling figures looming out in front.
31 'O Christ, they're coming at us!' Bullets spat,
32 And he remembered his rifle...rapid fire...
33 And started blazing wildly...then a bang
34 Crumpled and spun him sideways, knocked him out
35 To grunt and wriggle: none heeded him; he choked
36 And fought the flapping **veils** of smothering gloom,
37 Lost in a blurred confusion of yells and groans...
38 Down, and down, and down, he sank and drowned,
39 Bleeding to death. The counter-attack had failed.

THINK QUESTIONS   CA-CCSS: CA.RL.9-10.1, CA.L.9-10.4a, CA.L.9-10.4d

1. Refer to one or more details from the text to support your understanding of who the speaker of the poem is and what the speaker describes in the first six lines of the poem. Base your answers on evidence that is directly stated or that you have inferred from clues in the text.

2. What does the speaker describe in the last seven lines of the first stanza? Write two or three sentences that explain the images the speaker uses to paint a picture of the scene.

3. Write four or five sentences exploring the different responses of the infantryman and the officer who are participating in the counter-attack. Whose death is described in the third stanza? Support your answer with textual evidence.

4. Use context to determine the meaning of the word **blear** as it is used in line 15 of "Counter-Attack." Consult a print or digital dictionary to find the part of speech and the precise meaning of the word. Write your definition of "blear" and explain how you figured out its meaning.

5. Remembering that the word **veil** comes from the Latin *velum,* meaning "cloth, covering, or curtain," use the context clues provided in the text to determine the meaning of **veils,** as it is used in line 36 of "Counter-Attack." Write your definition of "veils" and tell how you determined the meaning of the word. Then confirm your inferred meaning in a print or digital dictionary.

CLOSE READ

CA-CCSS: CA.RL.9-10.1, CA.RL.9-10.2, CA.RL.9-10.3, CA.RL.9-10.4, CA.RL.9-10.5, CA.RL.9-10.6, CA.W.9-10.2a, CA.W.9-10.2b, CA.W.9-10.4, CA.W.9-10.5, CA.W.9-10.6, CA.W.9-10.9a, CA.W.9-10.10

Reread the poem "Counter-Attack." As you reread, complete the Focus Questions below. Then use your answers and annotations from the questions to help you complete the Writing Prompt.

FOCUS QUESTIONS

1. Describe the overall poetic structure of "Counter-Attack." How many stanzas and lines does the poet use? What features do you notice about the lines of the poem? What does this structure indicate about the poet's purpose for writing? Highlight specific evidence from the text and make annotations to explain your response.

2. What does the poet compare the dawn to in stanza 1 of the poem? How does this comparison connect to the theme (or message) of the poem? Use the annotation tool to make inferences about the text and its deeper meaning. Support your answer with textual evidence and make annotations to explain your answer.

3. How does the tone of the poem shift in the last line of stanza 1? What does this shift in tone reveal about the poet's attitude toward the war? How does the poet connect this shift in tone to the images and emotions he creates in stanza 2? Highlight specific evidence from the text and make annotations to support your analysis.

4. How do the officer's actions and the events in stanza 3 connect to the tone of the poem developed in stanza 2? Which images in the final stanza relate to the poem's central theme? Support your answer with textual evidence and make annotations to explain your response.

5. What is the central theme (or message) of "Counter-Attack"? Based on what you know about Sassoon from reading or listening to the introduction to the poem, whom do you think he would hold responsible for the dire consequences of war? Make annotations and cite evidence from the poem to support your inferences about Sassoon's point of view about who is responsible for what happens in war.

WRITING PROMPT

Siegfried Sassoon served as a soldier in the British Army for all of World War I, and he saw the inhumanity of the war firsthand. What is the theme (or message) of his poem "Counter-Attack"? Write a brief informative essay explaining how the poetic structure and the tone help to convey the theme (or message) of the poem and the poet's attitude toward the war. Begin with a clear topic sentence, and support your writing with relevant evidence from the text. Maintain a formal style and an objective tone, and end your essay with a strong conclusion that supports the information or explanation you presented. Include in your conclusion an answer to this question: Can a poem about a century-old war have the same impact today as it did when it was written?

Please note that excerpts and passages in the StudySync® library and this workbook are intended as touchstones to generate interest in an author's work. The excerpts and passages do not substitute for the reading of entire texts, and StudySync® strongly recommends that students seek out and purchase the whole literary or informational work in order to experience it as the author intended. Links to online resellers are available in our digital library. In addition, complete works may be ordered through an authorized reseller by filling out and returning to StudySync® the order form enclosed in this workbook.

Reading & Writing Companion   **49**

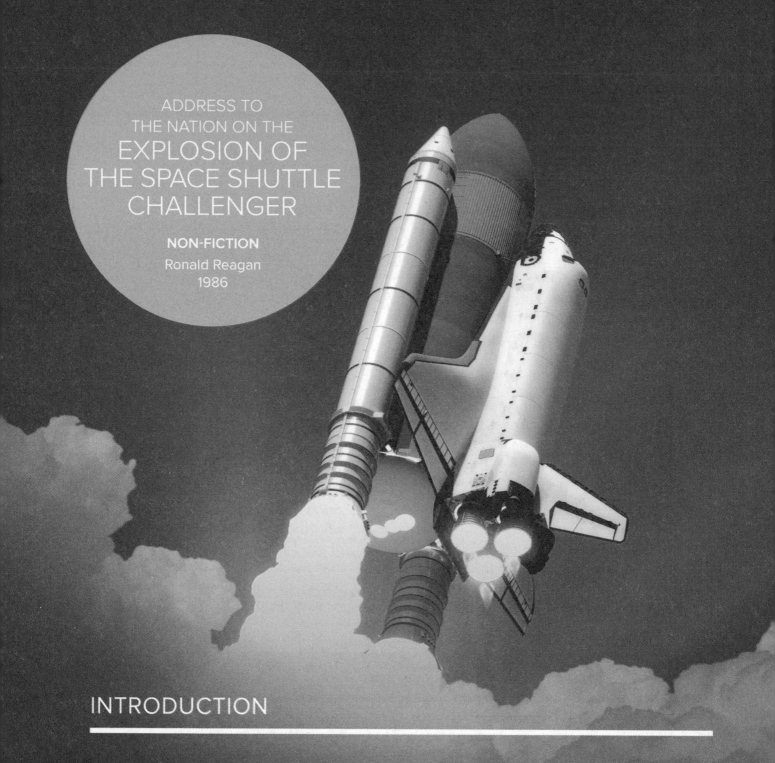

ADDRESS TO THE NATION ON THE EXPLOSION OF THE SPACE SHUTTLE CHALLENGER

NON-FICTION
Ronald Reagan
1986

INTRODUCTION

On January 28, 1986, millions of Americans watched on live TV as the Space Shuttle *Challenger* violently exploded just 73 seconds after takeoff, killing all seven people on board. It was the tenth mission for *Challenger*, but the first scheduled to carry an ordinary citizen into space, a teacher from New Hampshire named Christa McAuliffe. That evening, President Ronald Reagan addressed the nation, including the many school children who witnessed the disaster, and lauded the bravery of the fallen crew.

"Today is a day for mourning and remembering."

 FIRST READ

January 28, 1986

1   Ladies and gentlemen, I'd planned to speak to you tonight to report on the state of the Union, but the events of earlier today have led me to change those plans. Today is a day for mourning and remembering. Nancy and I are pained to the core by the tragedy of the shuttle *Challenger*. We know we share this pain with all of the people of our country. This is truly a national loss.

2   Nineteen years ago, almost to the day, we lost three astronauts in a terrible accident on the ground. But we've never lost an astronaut in flight; we've never had a tragedy like this. And perhaps we've forgotten the courage it took for the crew of the shuttle. But they, the *Challenger* Seven, were aware of the dangers, but overcame them and did their jobs brilliantly. We mourn seven heroes: Michael Smith, Dick Scobee, Judith Resnik, Ronald McNair, Ellison Onizuka, Gregory Jarvis, and Christa McAuliffe. We mourn their loss as a nation together.

3   For the families of the seven, we cannot bear, as you do, the full impact of this tragedy. But we feel the loss, and we're thinking about you so very much. Your loved ones were daring and brave, and they had that special **grace**, that special spirit that says, "Give me a challenge, and I'll meet it with joy." They had a hunger to explore the universe and discover its truths. They wished to serve, and they did. They served all of us. We've grown used to wonders in this century. It's hard to dazzle us. But for 25 years the United States space program has been doing just that. We've grown used to the idea of space, and perhaps we forget that we've only just begun. We're still pioneers. They, the members of the *Challenger* crew, were pioneers.

4   And I want to say something to the schoolchildren of America who were watching the live coverage of the shuttle's takeoff. I know it is hard to

Please note that excerpts and passages in the StudySync® library and this workbook are intended as touchstones to generate interest in an author's work. The excerpts and passages do not substitute for the reading of entire texts, and StudySync® strongly recommends that students seek out and purchase the whole literary or informational work in order to experience it as the author intended. Links to online resellers are available in our digital library. In addition, complete works may be ordered through an authorized reseller by filling out and returning to StudySync® the order form enclosed in this workbook.

Reading & Writing Companion

51

NOTES

understand, but sometimes painful things like this happen. It's all part of the process of exploration and discovery. It's all part of taking a chance and expanding man's **horizons**. The future doesn't belong to the fainthearted; it belongs to the brave. The *Challenger* crew was pulling us into the future, and we'll continue to follow them.

5   I've always had great faith in and respect for our space program, and what happened today does nothing to diminish it. We don't hide our space program. We don't keep secrets and cover things up. We do it all up front and in public. That's the way freedom is, and we wouldn't change it for a minute. We'll continue our quest in space. There will be more shuttle flights and more shuttle crews and, yes, more volunteers, more civilians, more teachers in space. Nothing ends here; our hopes and our journeys continue. I want to add that I wish I could talk to every man and woman who works for NASA or who worked on this mission and tell them: "Your dedication and **professionalism** have moved and impressed us for decades. And we know of your **anguish**. We share it."

6   There's a **coincidence** today. On this day 390 years ago, the great explorer Sir Francis Drake died aboard ship off the coast of Panama. In his lifetime the great frontiers were the oceans, and an historian later said, "He lived by the sea, died on it, and was buried in it." Well, today we can say of the *Challenger* crew: Their dedication was, like Drake's, complete.

7   The crew of the space shuttle *Challenger* honored us by the manner in which they lived their lives. We will never forget them, nor the last time we saw them, this morning, as they prepared for their journey and waved goodbye and "slipped the surly bonds of earth" to "touch the face of God."

THINK QUESTIONS   CA-CCSS: CA.RI.9-10.1, CA.RI.9-10.4, CA.L.9-10.4a, CA.RL.9-10.4

1. Refer to one or more details from the text to support your understanding of the significance of the Space Shuttle tragedy. What words and phrases in the first two paragraphs indicate this significance?

2. Use details from the text to write two or three sentences detailing how President Reagan describes the astronauts.

3. Write two or three sentences explaining how President Reagan feels about the space program. What details does he offer to support his ideas? Cite textual evidence in your answer.

4. Use context to determine the meaning of the word **horizons** as it is used in this speech. Write your definition of "horizons" here and tell how you found it.

5. Remembering that the Latin prefix *co-* means "together," use the context clues provided in the passage to determine the meaning of **coincidence**. Write your definition of "coincidence" here and tell how you got it.

CLOSE READ
CA-CCSS: CA.RI.9-10.1, CA.RI.9-10.2, CA.RI.9-10.4, CA.RI.9-10.6, CA.RI.9-10.7, CA.W.9-10.2a, CA.W.9-10.2b, CA.W.9-10.4, CA.W.9-10.5, CA.W.9-10.6, CA.W.9-10.9b, CA.W.9-10.10

Reread President Reagan's speech about the space shuttle disaster. As you reread, complete the Focus Questions below. Then use your answers and annotations from the questions to help you complete the Writing Prompt.

FOCUS QUESTIONS

1. Which words and phrases in the first two paragraphs help establish the topic of the speech? Highlight evidence from the text and make annotations to explain your answer.

2. Speeches often use formal, elevated language to make a point. What does the formal, elevated language in paragraph 3 help to emphasize? Highlight evidence from the text and make annotations to support your answer.

3. In paragraphs 4 and 5, what argument does the president make about the space program? What makes speech a good medium for expressing this argument? Highlight evidence from the text and make annotations to support your ideas.

4. Highlight the quotation in paragraph 6. What ideas does this quotation help the president to express about the *Challenger* astronauts? Make annotations to explain the president's ideas in your own words.

5. Throughout the address, President Reagan expresses his confidence in the space program, and he compliments the people who work for NASA. How do his words relate to the idea of having responsibility for what we create? Highlight textual evidence and make annotations to explain your ideas.

WRITING PROMPT

Write a response in which you analyze the choice of words and phrases in the speech. Which words and phrases would be unlikely to appear in a newspaper or magazine article or in a news broadcast? Why are they included in the speech? Support your answer with textual evidence.

ADDRESS TO STUDENTS AT MOSCOW STATE UNIVERSITY

NON-FICTION
Ronald Reagan
1988

INTRODUCTION

I n May 1988, during the final year of Ronald Reagan's presidency and just one year after he admonished Gorbachev to tear down the Berlin wall, the president met with the USSR's leader in Moscow to discuss arms reductions. During his visit, he delivered a stirring speech to students at Moscow State University setting forth his vision for the expansion of liberty across the globe. Highlighting the opportunities afforded by freedom and entrepreneurship, Reagan focused on the advances of technology in the United States, as well as Russian contributions to world culture.

"The key is freedom—freedom of thought, freedom of information, freedom of communication."

 FIRST READ

 NOTES

1   As you know, I've come to Moscow to meet with one of your most distinguished graduates. In this, our fourth summit, General Secretary Gorbachev and I have spent many hours together, and I feel that we're getting to know each other well. Our discussions, of course, have been focused primarily on many of the important issues of the day, issues I want to touch on with you in a few moments. But first I want to take a little time to talk to you much as I would to any group of university students in the United States. I want to talk not just of the realities of today but of the possibilities of tomorrow.

2   Standing here before a mural of your revolution, I want to talk about a very different revolution that is taking place right now, quietly sweeping the globe without bloodshed or conflict. Its effects are peaceful, but they will **fundamentally** alter our world, shatter old assumptions, and reshape our lives. It's easy to underestimate because it's not accompanied by banners or fanfare. It's been called the technological or information revolution, and as its emblem, one might take the tiny silicon chip, no bigger than a fingerprint. One of these chips has more computing power than a roomful of old-style computers.

3   As part of an exchange program, we now have an **exhibition** touring your country that shows how information technology is transforming our lives— replacing manual labor with robots, forecasting weather for farmers, or mapping the genetic code of DNA for medical researchers. These microcomputers today aid the design of everything from houses to cars to spacecraft; they even design better and faster computers. They can translate English into Russian or enable the blind to read or help Michael Jackson produce on one synthesizer the sounds of a whole orchestra. Linked by a network of satellites and fiber-optic cables, one individual with a desktop computer and a telephone commands resources unavailable to the largest governments just a few years ago.

4   Like a chrysalis, we're emerging from the economy of the Industrial Revolution—an economy confined to and limited by the Earth's physical resources—into, as one economist titled his book, "The Economy in Mind," in which there are no bounds on human imagination and the freedom to create is the most precious natural resource. Think of that little computer chip. Its value isn't in the sand from which it is made but in the microscopic architecture designed into it by ingenious human minds. Or take the example of the satellite relaying this broadcast around the world, which replaces thousands of tons of copper mined from the Earth and molded into wire. In the new economy, human invention increasingly makes physical resources obsolete. We're breaking through the material conditions of existence to a world where man creates his own destiny. Even as we explore the most advanced reaches of science, we're returning to the age-old wisdom of our culture, a wisdom contained in the book of Genesis in the Bible: In the beginning was the spirit and it was from this spirit that the material abundance of creation issued forth.

5   But progress is not **foreordained**. The key is freedom—freedom of thought, freedom of information, freedom of communication. The renowned scientist, scholar, and founding father of this university, Mikhail Lomonosov, knew that. "It is common knowledge," he said, "that the achievements of science are considerable and rapid, particularly once the yoke of slavery is cast off and replaced by the freedom of philosophy."

6   You know, one of the first contacts between your country and mine took place between Russian and American explorers. The Americans were members of Cook's last voyage on an expedition searching for an Arctic passage; on the island of Unalaska, they came upon the Russians, who took them in, and together with the native inhabitants, held a prayer service on the ice.

7   The explorers of the modern era are the entrepreneurs, men with vision, with the courage to take risks and faith enough to brave the unknown. These entrepreneurs and their small enterprises are responsible for almost all the economic growth in the United States. They are the prime movers of the technological revolution. In fact, one of the largest personal computer firms in the United States was started by two college students, no older than you, in the garage behind their home. Some people, even in my own country, look at the riot of experiment that is the free market and see only waste. What of all the entrepreneurs that fail? Well, many do, particularly the successful ones; often several times. And if you ask them the secret of their success they'll tell you it's all that they learned in their struggles along the way; yes, it's what they learned from failing. Like an athlete in competition or a scholar in pursuit of the truth, experience is the greatest teacher.

NOTES

8 And that's why it's so hard for government planners, no matter how sophisticated, to ever substitute for millions of individuals working night and day to make their dreams come true.

. . .

9 We Americans make no secret of our belief in freedom. In fact, it's something of a national pastime. Every 4 years the American people choose a new President, and 1988 is one of those years. At one point there were 13 major candidates running in the two major parties, not to mention all the others, including the Socialist and Libertarian candidates—all trying to get my job.

10 About 1,000 local television stations, 8,500 radio stations, and 1,700 daily newspapers—each one an independent, private enterprise, fiercely independent of the Government—report on the candidates, grill them in interviews, and bring them together for debates. In the end, the people vote; they decide who will be the next President.

11 But freedom doesn't begin or end with elections. Go to any American town, to take just an example, and you'll see dozens of churches, representing many different beliefs—in many places, synagogues and mosques—and you'll see families of every conceivable nationality worshiping together. Go into any schoolroom, and there you will see children being taught the Declaration of Independence, that they are endowed by their Creator with certain unalienable rights—among them life, liberty, and the pursuit of happiness—that no government can justly deny; the guarantees in their Constitution for freedom of speech, freedom of assembly, and freedom of religion.

12 Go into any courtroom, and there will preside an independent judge, **beholden** to no government power. There every defendant has the right to a trial by a jury of his peers, usually 12 men and women—common citizens; they are the ones, the only ones, who weigh the evidence and decide on guilt or innocence. In that court, the accused is innocent until proven guilty, and the word of a policeman or any official has no greater legal standing than the word of the accused.

13 Go to any university campus, and there you'll find an open, sometimes heated discussion of the problems in American society and what can be done to correct them. Turn on the television, and you'll see the legislature conducting the business of government right there before the camera, debating and voting on the legislation that will become the law of the land. March in any demonstration, and there are many of them; the people's right of assembly is guaranteed in the Constitution and protected by the police. Go into any union hall, where the members know their right to strike is protected by law. As a

matter of fact, one of the many jobs I had before this one was being president of a union, the Screen Actors Guild. I led my union out on strike, and I'm proud to say we won.

14 But freedom is more even than this. Freedom is the right to question and change the established way of doing things. It is the continuing revolution of the marketplace. It is the understanding that allows us to recognize shortcomings and seek solutions. It is the right to put forth an idea, scoffed at by the experts, and watch it catch fire among the people. It is the right to dream—to follow your dream or stick to your conscience, even if you're the only one in a sea of doubters. Freedom is the recognition that no single person, no single authority or government has a monopoly on the truth, but that every individual life is infinitely precious, that every one of us put on this world has been put there for a reason and has something to offer.

. . .

15 But I hope you know I go on about these things not simply to **extol** the virtues of my own country but to speak to the true greatness of the heart and soul of your land. Who, after all, needs to tell the land of Dostoyevski about the quest for truth, the home of Kandinski and Scriabin about imagination, the rich and noble culture of the Uzbek man of letters Alisher Navoi about beauty and heart? The great culture of your diverse land speaks with a glowing passion to all humanity. Let me cite one of the most eloquent contemporary passages on human freedom. It comes, not from the literature of America, but from this country, from one of the greatest writers of the 20th century, Boris Pasternak, in the novel "Dr. Zhivago." He writes: "I think that if the beast who sleeps in man could be held down by threats—any kind of threat, whether of jail or of retribution after death—then the highest emblem of humanity would be the lion tamer in the circus with his whip, not the prophet who sacrificed himself. But this is just the point—what has for centuries raised man above the beast is not the cudgel, but an inward music—the irresistible power of unarmed truth."

THINK QUESTIONS CA-CCSS: CA.RI.9-10.1, CA.RI.9-10.4, CA.L.9-10.4a

1. President Reagan says that the technological or information revolution will "alter our world" and "reshape our lives." What changes does the president note are already happening? Support your answer with textual evidence.

2. Use details from the text to write two or three sentences about the evidence President Reagan offers to support his claim that freedom is "a national pastime" for Americans.

3. What connection does President Reagan make between freedom and progress? Support your answer with textual evidence and your own inferences.

4. You may remember that the Anglo-German prefix *for-* means "before" or "first," and the Latin root *ord* refers to order. Use these roots and the context clues provided in the passage to determine the meaning of **foreordained**. Write your definition of "foreordained" here and explain how you arrived at it.

5. Use context to determine the meaning of the word **extol** as it is used in "Address to Students at Moscow State University." Write your definition of "extol" here and explain how you arrived at it.

CLOSE READ

CA-CCSS: CA.RI.9-10.1, CA.RI.9-10.2, CA.RI.9-10.3, CA.RI.9-10.4, CA.RI.9-10.6, CA.RI.9-10.9, CA.L.9-10.4a, CA.W.9-10.1a,
CA.W.9-10.1b, CA.W.9-10.4, CA.W.9-10.5, CA.W.9-10.6, CA.W.9-10.9b, CA.W.9-10.10

Reread President Reagan's speech to the students in Moscow. As you reread, complete the Focus Questions below. Then use your answers and annotations from the questions to help you complete the Writing Prompt.

FOCUS QUESTIONS

1. In paragraph 2 of his Moscow address, President Reagan introduces the word "revolution." He compares and contrasts the Russian Revolution of 1917 ("your revolution") with the "technological or information revolution" of his own day. How are these two revolutions alike? How are they different? What exactly does he mean by calling the changes in technology a "revolution"? Support your answer with textual evidence and make annotations to support your explanations.

2. Summarize President Reagan's main points about daily life in America. What is his purpose in speaking at such length about Americans' experiences with politics, law, home, work, and community? Highlight evidence from the text and make annotations to explain your ideas.

3. In the second-to-last paragraph of the speech, how does the president define freedom? What ideas from earlier in the speech does this section help to reinforce? Highlight evidence from the text and make annotations to support your explanations.

4. In the final paragraph of the speech, President Reagan quotes from Boris Pasternak's *Dr. Zhivago*. Summarize Pasternak's main point. How does Pasternak's message relate to the main message Reagan wants to convey to the Moscow students? Highlight evidence from the text and make annotations to support your answer.

5. In this speech, President Reagan alludes to the openness of the American system of government. What relationship do you see between openness and responsibility? Highlight evidence from the text and make annotations to support your answer.

WRITING PROMPT

Compare and contrast the main themes and concepts contained in "Address to Students at Moscow State University" and in "Address to the Nation on the Explosion of the Space Shuttle *Challenger*." What claims about society and progress do both speeches make? What kinds of details do the speeches use to support the claims? Are the details similar or different? Finally, which speech is the more effective or convincing? Support your answer with evidence from both speeches.

DE-EXTINCTION:
THE SCIENCE AND
ETHICS OF BRINGING LOST
SPECIES BACK TO LIFE

NON-FICTION

2014

INTRODUCTION

Advances in biological science may soon make it possible to bring animals and plants back from extinction. This prospect has wildly exciting implications: by reversing extinction, we could restore biodiversity to the planet and potentially solve some of our environmental problems. However, de-extinction has the potential for dangerous, evenly deadly consequences. Is this a case of "just because we can doesn't mean we should?" Read two essays that explore the issue from different sides and decide for yourself. Which argument do you feel is more convincing?

"What sounds like science fiction may soon be scientific fact."

FIRST READ

The Science and Ethics of De-Extinction: Should We Recreate Lost Species?

Point: "De-Extinction Is Ethical, and Compelled by Science"

1   Which of the following animals would you most like to see up close and in person? Would it be the dodo, those flightless, squat birds from Mauritius? Sadly, dodos were victims of overhunting and the destruction of their habitat and now they are extinct. The last one died in the late 1800's. How about the passenger pigeon? This species went from being the most common bird in North America to being hunted to extinction. The last passenger pigeon died in an Illinois zoo in 1914. Why not meet a saber-toothed tiger, a creature as fierce as its name suggests? Sorry: this species vanished from Earth more than 10,000 years ago. Once a creature is extinct, it is gone forever...or is it?

2   What sounds like science fiction may soon be scientific fact. De-extinction, or bringing back extinct animals and plants, is becoming increasingly possible. That is because sci-en-tists are now working to develop technology that will enable them to clone extinct species and bring them back to life. But just because we can do something, should we do it? Yes! Scientists should vigorously pursue their experiments in de-extinction. People who say that de-extinction is unethical are wrong. Here's why.

3   The first ethical reason for bringing creatures back from extinction is that it helps preserve biodiversity, repair damaged ecosystems, and preserve the world for future generations. Stewart Brand, creator of the *Whole Earth Catalog*, argued in favor of de-extinction in *National Geographic* magazine. Brand described how some long-gone species were especially important to their region, calling these species "keystones" after the central stone at the top of an arch. Brand says: "Woolly mammoths, for instance, were the dominant herbivore of the mammoth steppe in the far north, once the largest biome on Earth. In their absence, the grasslands they helped sustain were

replaced by species-poor tundra and boreal forest. Their return to the north would bring back carbon-fixing grass and reduce greenhouse-gas-releasing tundra."

4   Brand is not alone in his support of de-extinction for preserving biodiversity. "I think de-extinction can enrich conservation efforts," says Ryan Phelan, executive director of the Revive & Restore project at the Long Now Foundation. Phelan continues: "As controversial as all of it is, and possibly because it's controversial, it's going to help drive interest in [species loss], in a way that conservation by itself couldn't do...The species that we are talking about bringing back, they really are part of the continuum of life. And I think that's the real power in what we are trying to do. We're calling attention to the extinction threat."

5   Since every species is linked to every other one, resurrecting extinct animals may help us control the ravages of global warming and human overpopulation, too. De-extinction might even be able to repair some of the damage we have **incurred** by cutting down rainforests and building too many homes. De-extinction can certainly help restore traditional values, strengthen families, and encourage education. It is a win-win proposition.

6   What about the price tag? A scientific endeavor of this complexity and magnitude may not come cheaply, but it is worth the cost. De-extinction is an ethical use of research funding because it helps us undo harm that humans have caused in the past, such as the appalling slaughter of the passenger pigeon. In his article "The Story of the Passenger Pigeon," author Clive Ponting notes that passenger pigeons were so common 150 years ago that a hunter could kill 30-40 birds with a single bullet. Soon, the birds were hunted to death for food. On just one day in 1860, over 200,000 birds were killed and shipped from the Midwest to the East. By 1914, a species that had once numbered five billion had been totally **eradicated**. Don't we owe it to these harmless, beautiful birds to bring them back?

7   Finally, bringing back extinct creatures advances science, which helps us in myriad ways. For instance, people have been critical about the space program since its inception, saying that we would never get anything useful from blasting into the skies. However, in a speech celebrating NASA's 50th anniversary, NASA administrator Michael Griffin noted that the technology to come out of the space program has greatly improved our lives. Thanks to space exploration, we have weather satellites that warn us of coming storms, heart defibrillators that save lives, personal computers that foster communication, bigger and better crops, and much more. The genome manipulation used in de-extinction research might bring about even more marvels. Maybe these experiments will lead to a cure for cancer or let us live to be 200! We won't know unless we try.

NOTES

Counterpoint: "De-Extinction Is Immoral, and Bad Science All Around"

8   A scientist cobbles together a creature from old body parts and brings it to life. The scientist is aghast at his creation, a horrific monster. The monster, shunned by the human race, kills his creator's brother in an attempt to punish his creator. An innocent young girl is convicted of the crime and executed. Can it get any worse? Yes, it can. Fortunately, this story is fiction, the plot of the novel *Frankenstein* by Mary Shelley. Make-believe can become reality, thanks to research on de-extinction. De-extinction is immoral, unethical, and dangerous. It should not be pursued.

9   To start, it is unethical for humans to mess with Mother Nature because, as the story of *Frankenstein* illustrates, we have no idea what **havoc** we might cause in doing so. Many extinct creatures were fearsome killers that would be very dangerous to humans. The extinct saber-toothed tiger, for instance, was a terrifying predator armed with razor-sharp long sharp teeth used to tear open its prey. We should be glad we are not living in the Ice Age and facing off against such a dangerous creature! Fortunately, de-extinction of such long-ago creatures is not yet possible, but *National Geographic* reports that a different kind of lethal organism *has* been brought back—the flu virus of 1918, which killed 50 million people. Scientists are keeping the virus under lock and key, so no one has been exposed. Extinct animal predators like the saber-toothed tiger are dangerous enough, but what if the tigers or other animals also bring back treacherous viruses on their bodies? The harm to humanity cannot be calculated.

10   Let's imagine that scientists do succeed in bringing back ancient creatures through de-extinction. To do so, scientists would create multiple creatures from a single piece of genetic material. As a result, the creatures would lack genetic variety, which would be unfair to the creatures because genetic variety is essential to survival. These creatures would be less capable of adapting to new challenges and so they would be **susceptible** to all sorts of threats. The cloned sheep Dolly illustrates this. Born in 1996, she lived until 2003, a total of six and a half years. Sheep can live to be twelve years old, but Dolly was euthanized after only half her natural life span because she had severe arthritis and lung disease. Some sources say her diseases were caused by cloning; others because she was raised indoors rather than outdoors. We don't know why her lifespan was half of what it should have been, which is arguably reason enough to reject de-extinction through cloning.

11   It is likely that de-extinction cannot be accomplished in a humane way, which is troublesome. Let's return to Dolly as an example. "From 277 cell fusions, 29 early embryos developed and were implanted into 13 surrogate mothers. But only one pregnancy went to full term," according to Animal Research. Info. That

amounts to thirteen sheep that were used to clone just one lamb, a creature that was not extinct. How many elephants, serving as surrogate mothers, would it take bring back the **primeval** woolly mammoth? Conservationist Rory Young, interviewed in the *Huffington Post*, is "absolutely convinced" that African elephants could be extinct in less than a decade if they are not protected. Using them to incubate wooly mammoths hardly qualifies as protection—it is not ethical to harm one species to bring back another.

12 Here is yet another reason why de-extinction is immoral: bringing back extinct creatures distracts us from the real and pressing environmental issues we face today. De-extinction research, not to mention the actual process of cloning these creatures from their DNA, costs a prohibitive amount of money. This funding can be put to far better use by finding ways to prevent extinction in the first place through saving natural habitats, reducing pollution, and researching climate change. As Bob Strauss, a dinosaur expert, writes in "De-Extinction—The Resurrection of Extinct Animals," "De-extinction is a PR gimmick that detracts from real environmental issues. What is the point of resurrecting the Gastric-Brooding Frog when hundreds of amphibian species are on the brink of succumbing to global warming? A successful de-extinction effort may give people the false, and dangerous, impression that scientists have 'solved' all of our environmental problems."

13 The creatures that scientists bring back would require food, so we would have to alter the land and introduce new—perhaps previously extinct—crops. These new crops would interfere with the habitats of existing species, plus the returned animals would also need safe homes, further displacing the existing species. It would be a vicious cycle.

14 Finally, there are significant reasons why some creatures went extinct in the first place. With the exception of animals driven to extinction by humans, such as passenger pigeons, extinct animals are extinct for valid reasons. In some cases their environments changed so that food and water supplies decreased or disappeared. And what happens if we bring back extinct creatures like woolly mammoths and saber-toothed tigers and humans hunt them back into extinction a second time? According to "8 Endangered Species Still Hunted," great white sharks, cheetahs, polar bears, and hippos are just a few of the vulnerable species hunted despite laws designed to protect them.

15 Being *able* to do something doesn't mean we should do it. Where will allowing de-extinction lead? Will scientists bring back a few oddities for show? This is unethical, but establishing a stable population and returning it to the wild is even more unethical because we have no idea what impact it would have on the environment. If we resurrect extinct species, humans might become extinct! And would saber-toothed tigers and wooly mammoths want to bring *us* back?

THINK QUESTIONS CA-CCSS: CA.RI.9-10.1, CA.L.9-10.4a, CA.L.9-10.4d

1. The specific issue of de-extinction is part of a broader issue that faces humanity. What is that broader issue, and where in the text of the debate does each author address it? Cite specific passages in your response.

2. What is each author's perspective on the idea that "just because we can doesn't mean we should"? Why is this a relevant idea to explore in relation to the issue of de-extinction and other possibilities created by scientific advancements? Cite text evidence in your answer.

3. This debate is an example of persuasive writing. What role does information play in it? Provide specific examples from the debate.

4. Use context to determine the meaning of the word **susceptible** as it is used in "De-Extinction: The Science and Ethics of Bringing Lost Species Back to Life." Write your definition of "susceptible" here and tell how you found it.

5. Use the context clues provided in the passage to determine the meaning of the word **eradicated**. Write your definition of "eradicated" here and tell how you got it.

CLOSE READ

CA-CCSS: CA.RI.9-10.1, CA.RI.9-10.5, CA.RI.9-10.8, CA.W.9-10.1a, CA.W.9-10.1b, CA.W.9-10.4, CA.W.9-10.5, CA.W.9-10.6, CA.W.9-10.9b, CA.W.9-10.10

Reread the debate about de-extinction. As you reread, complete the Focus Questions below. Then use your answers and annotations from the questions to help you complete the Writing Prompt.

FOCUS QUESTIONS

1. How does the Point argument, entitled "De-Extinction Is Ethical, and Compelled by Science," use problem and solution structure in the fifth paragraph? What is the problem, and what solution is presented? Is the logic used to support this problem and solution sound? Why or why not?

2. Review the fourth paragraph of the Point argument and the fifth paragraph of the Counterpoint argument, entitled "De-Extinction Is Immoral, and Bad Science All Around." What strategy do both arguments use in these paragraphs to support their claims? Identify the claim and evidence in each paragraph.

3. What relevance does a discussion about Dolly the sheep have in the third paragraph of the Counterpoint argument? How does this subtopic fit into the structure of the argument as a whole?

4. How does the sixth paragraph of the Counterpoint argument use cause and effect text structure in support of a point?

5. Based on ideas presented throughout the debate, what responsibility does each author think humans bear for the world in its present state, and how should people best address that responsibility in the future? Address similarities and differences in the two authors' points of view.

WRITING PROMPT

In your estimation, which argument—Point or Counterpoint—won the debate in the selection "De-Extinction: The Science and Ethics of Bringing Lost Species Back to Life"? In a structured argument of approximately one page, explain why you think either the Point or the Counterpoint argument is more successful than the other. Make sure to address the amount and relevance of the evidence in each essay, as well as the overall validity of the reasoning in both arguments and whether or not they contain any fallacious reasoning. In what way did the more successful argument best use text structure and persuasive techniques to help organize and enhance its claims? Cite specific passages from *both* the Point and the Counterpoint sides of the de-extinction debate as evidence for your evaluation.

Please note that excerpts and passages in the StudySync® library and this workbook are intended as touchstones to generate interest in an author's work. The excerpts and passages do not substitute for the reading of entire texts, and StudySync® strongly recommends that students seek out and purchase the whole literary or informational work in order to experience it as the author intended. Links to online resellers are available in our digital library. In addition, complete works may be ordered through an authorized reseller by filling out and returning to StudySync® the order form enclosed in this workbook.

Reading & Writing Companion 67

FATE OR FOOLISHNESS

English Language
Development

FICTION

INTRODUCTION

An accident creates a violent element that destroys half the planet and threatens what remains. Could an unlikely pair of heroes save the day? Follow along as a scientist and his computerized pet raven set out to return things to normal.

"Tonight I would lose my friend forever."

FIRST READ

1   In those days, every human unit was warned to stay away from the EDGE, the Eastern Dangerous Galaxy Enclosure. The EDGE existed since the twenty-first century when a ghastly event happened. There had been an underground tunnel experiment in progress when an explosion happened aboveground. The explosion created a vast **chasm** and cracked open tunnels. The planet shook, releasing random blasts of bright, flaming energy that **collided** violently in the atmosphere. Half the planet was destroyed. Since then, no one has entered the area of the catastrophe that we call the singularity. It has an intense gravitational pull. Nothing can escape from it. The EDGE was the barrier set up to isolate the **calamity**.

2   Once upon a midnight dreary, I foolishly believed that I could repair the planet and destroy the EDGE. In those days, human units had created machines that were advanced for their time. The machines were programmed well. They did many things for human units. No longer did the units have to know mathematics because the machines calculated for them. No longer did they need dictionaries because the machines "knew" the definition and spelling of every word. But, according to the designers and manufacturers, the machines could not think for themselves. They simply followed the directives of their makers.

3   I took a different approach with my experiments. I focused on true "artificial intelligence," and so built Lenore, a bird-like thinking machine. At first visitors to my laboratory laughed in mockery. "A raven is such a **bizarre** pet for a scientist!" They did not recognize that Lenore was not an ordinary raven. They could not guess that she would change their existence. I taught Lenore to make decisions, to take chances, to be brave. She became my friend, one that I loved dearly.

4   This explains why I was standing on a desolate plain near the EDGE. It was a dark and stormy night. Sizzling bits of energy seemed to float above the singularity. No plant, nor tree, nor blade of grass grew on the bleak plain. The earth was scorched, stripped bare. The singularity sucked the energy from all

living creatures. Merciless blasts of wind rocked my body, but Lenore rested safely under my jacket. **Ominous** cracking and creaking sounds, which had neither beginning nor end, filled me with terror. Yet, I had come to fulfill my destiny. Perhaps I was correct in my actions; I will never know.

5   The harsh wind tore at my jacket. The beating of my fearful heart drowned out the relentless sounds of the singularity. I moved as close as I dared to the flashing, rippling nightmare that had ruined my beloved planet. Slowly, with shaking fingers, I opened my jacket. Lenore looked at me, wide-eyed, unafraid. Tonight I would lose my friend forever. Yet, I knew if she were successful, my planet would be healed.

6   I eased Lenore out and placed her on my shoulder. I whispered one final goodbye and then shouted, "Lenore, do what you must!" She rose into the turbulent air, strong against the violent wind. Her instructions were simple; she was to fly into the singularity and do what needed to be done to destroy it. She could think and reason, so she would know what to do once inside. She circled twice and flew straight into the center. Suddenly, flames exploded, feeding on the oxygen in the air. I struggled to breathe. Horrid shrieks roared and howled. Time and space flew apart, breaking into a million pieces before slamming back together with an ear-splitting scream.

7   The singularity disappeared. The desolate plain was gone, too. I was standing next to an apple tree, and somewhere a raven was making a cawing sound. Stunned, I began walking, not knowing or caring where I was. I picked an apple from the tree and took a bite. Taking a deep breath I looked around. I was in a beautiful garden. It seemed like now there would be a new beginning.

USING LANGUAGE CA-CCSS: ELD.PII.9-10.4.Ex

Read each sentence from the text and choose the noun phrase. Remember that a noun phrase includes a noun and an adjective and/or phrase that modifies the noun.

1. "They did many things for human units."

    ○ did many things
    ○ things for human units

2. "I focused on true 'artificial intelligence,'" and so built Lenore, a bird-like thinking machine."

    ○ true "artificial intelligence"
    ○ and so built

3. "At first visitors to my laboratory laughed in mockery."

    ○ visitors to my laboratory
    ○ laughed in mockery

4. "The singularity sucked the energy from all living creatures."

    ○ the singularity sucked
    ○ energy from all living creatures

5. "The beating of my fearful heart drowned out the relentless sounds of the singularity."

    ○ beating of my fearful heart
    ○ drowned out the relentless

6. "Her instructions were simple..."

    ○ Her instructions
    ○ were simple

7. "Suddenly, flames exploded, feeding on the oxygen in the air."

    ○ exploded, feeding on
    ○ oxygen in the air

8. "I picked an apple from the tree and took a bite."

    ○ I picked
    ○ apple from the tree

MEANINGFUL INTERACTIONS CA-CCSS: ELD.PI.9-10.1.Ex, ELD.PI.9-10.6.a.Ex

In the created text, "Fate or Foolishness," the author structures the plot through cause-and-effect relationships. Review the paragraphs from the text. Then identify the cause-and-effect relationships. You can use the speaking frames below to help express your ideas in the discussion. Remember to make coherent, well-articulated comments. Then, use the self-assessment rubric to evaluate your participation in the discussion.

3 I took a different approach with my experiments. I focused on true "artificial intelligence," and so built Lenore, a bird-like thinking machine. At first visitors to my laboratory laughed in mockery. "A raven is such a bizarre pet for a scientist!" They did not recognize that Lenore was not an ordinary raven. They could not guess that she would change their existence. I taught Lenore to make decisions, to take chances, to be brave. She became my friend, one that I loved dearly.

5 The harsh wind tore at my jacket. The beating of my fearful heart drowned out the relentless sounds of the singularity. I moved as close as I dared to the flashing, rippling nightmare that had ruined my beloved planet. Slowly, with shaking fingers, I opened my jacket. Lenore looked at me, wide-eyed, unafraid. Tonight I would lose my friend forever. Yet, I knew if she were successful, my planet would be healed.

- The narrator's approach to the experiment is different than the others before him because . . .

- What is the **cause** of the loss of his friend Lenore?

- What **effect** does he hope to have in losing his friend?

- In your opinion, is the desired **effect** worth the sacrifice of losing his friend?

- Some other **cause-and-effect relationships** in the text are . . .

SELF-ASSESSMENT RUBRIC CA-CCSS: ELD.PI.9-10.1.Ex, ELD.PI.9-10.6.a.Ex

	4 I did this well.	3 I did this pretty well.	2 I did this a little bit.	1 I did not do this.
I expressed my ideas clearly.				
I supported my ideas using evidence from the text.				
I explained how the writer used cause-and-effect relationships in the text.				
I provided coherent, well-articulated comments.				

REREAD

Reread paragraphs 1–4 of "Fate or Foolishness." After you reread, complete the Using Language and Meaningful Interactions activities.

⚙ USING LANGUAGE CA-CCSS: ELD.PII.9-10.5.Fx

Read each sentence based on the text. Choose the adverb to correctly complete each sentence.

1. The narrator worked _____ to build Lenore.

   ○ carefully
   ○ studied

2. Most of the planet was destroyed _____.

   ○ instantly
   ○ vacancy

3. The plain near the singularity was scorched _____.

   ○ boundary
   ○ completely

4. The strong, fierce wind pushed _____ against his body.

   ○ forcefully
   ○ quality

5. Lenore rested _____ under his jacket.

   ○ activity
   ○ safely

6. The singularity _____ disappeared.

   ○ finally
   ○ area

7. The narrator walked _____ through the apple orchard.

   ○ happily
   ○ journey

MEANINGFUL INTERACTIONS CA-CCSS: ELD.PI.9-10.1.Ex, ELD.PI.9-10.6.b.Ex

Work with partners or small groups to identify the descriptions of the inventor's actions, speech, and personality in the story. You can use the speaking frames below to help express your ideas in the discussion. Remember to follow turn-taking rules during the discussion and affirm others' opinions. Then, use the self-assessment rubric to evaluate your participation in the discussion.

- Based on the word/phrase/sentence . . . , I infer that the narrator . . .

- The word/phrase/sentence . . . also suggests that the narrator . . .

- The narrator can be described as . . .

- I agree/disagree with your point about the narrator because . . .

 SELF-ASSESSMENT RUBRIC CA-CCSS: ELD.PI.9-10.1.Ex, ELD.PI.9-10.6.b.Ex

	4 I did this well.	3 I did this pretty well.	2 I did this a little bit.	1 I did not do this.
I expressed my ideas clearly.				
I supported my ideas using evidence from the text.				
I made inferences about the inventor based on his thoughts, actions, interactions, and dialogue.				
I took turns sharing my ideas with the group.				

 REREAD

Reread paragraphs 5–7 of "Fate or Foolishness." After you reread, complete the Using Language and Meaningful Interactions activities.

 USING LANGUAGE CA-CCSS: ELD.PI.9-10.6.c.Ex

Complete the chart on the right by using context clues to figure out the meaning of the bold word in each sentence from the text. Then write the meaning in the right column from the options.

Meaning Options		
moved suddenly	moved with force	in disbelief or shock
got up	form conclusions or make judgments	taking in

Sentences from the Text	Meaning
"The harsh wind **tore** at my jacket."	
"She **rose** into the turbulent air, strong against the violent wind."	
"She could think and **reason**, so she would know what to do once inside."	
"Suddenly, flames exploded, **feeding** on the oxygen in the air."	
"Time and space **flew** apart, breaking into a million pieces before slamming back together with an ear-splitting scream."	
"**Stunned**, I began walking, not knowing or caring where I was."	

 MEANINGFUL INTERACTIONS CA-CCSS: ELD.PI.9-10.11.b.Ex

In "Fate or Foolishness," the author writes about machines with artificial intelligence. Using the speaking frames, discuss whether or not humans should create computers or other machines with artificial intelligence. Remember to use a variety of modal expressions (*can, may, possibly/likely, could/would*) when sharing opinions.

- In my opinion, the use of artificial intelligence should/shouldn't be pursued **because** . . .

- It is *possible* these computers or machines *could* . . .

- Some benefits to the use of machines with artificial intelligence *can* be . . .

- Some drawbacks to the use of machines with artificial intelligence *may* be . . .

- I agree/disagree with others' opinions because . . .

THE SCIENCE OF GENETICALLY ALTERING FOODS: SHOULD WE DO IT?

English Language Development

NON-FICTION

INTRODUCTION

New technology promises healthier crops, with higher yield and greater nutritional value. But do these advances carry with them potential problems?

"Nature does not add a salmon gene to strawberry seeds."

 FIRST READ

 NOTES

Point: Genetic modification of plants is justified. It dramatically improves the quality and quantity of crops.

1   Genetic modification involves the **manipulation** of DNA to introduce a totally different gene. The action changes the original structure of the plant. Genetically **modified** crops are more resistant to diseases and pests. That resistance is appealing to farmers because insects alone cause huge crop losses every year. Losing crops means farmers make less money and less food is produced to feed the population.

2   Farmers have to use a lot of pesticides to protect their crops. The crops will obviously absorb some of these poisons. They will pass them on to the animals or humans that consume the crops. However, genetically modified plants would most likely need only one application of a pesticide. Farmers save time and money. In addition, not reapplying pesticides will help the environment.

3   The demand for improved crops is increasing worldwide. One reason for this increased demand is that genetically modified corn, cotton, and soybean seeds have larger crop yields. The seed developer claims five to eight percent more crops. The plants can also be modified to improve nutrition. Hunger could be eliminated in countries where malnutrition is a serious problem. For example, scientists are developing "golden rice." That rice will stimulate the body to develop vitamin A. The rice will improve the health of millions of children in underdeveloped countries. Without vitamin A, they will go blind.

4   Plants and animals have been modified throughout history with the help of science. For example, with crossbreeding, a single mustard **species** developed into broccoli, Brussels sprouts, and cabbage. Generations of plant breeding have improved taste, size, and yields of different foods. Those changes take time. On the other hand, genetic modification can change seeds in one generation.

5   The initial research and development of genetically modified crops are very expensive. That is true. However, the long-term benefits are well worth the initial cost. The seeds may be expensive, but farmers save on fewer pesticides. Farmers can grow larger, disease-resistant crops. Finally, more crops will eliminate world hunger.

Counterpoint: Genetic modification of plant material is both potentially **lethal** and dangerous.

6   Genetic modification introduces other elements to the DNA of plants, including bacteria and fungus. Those elements could have permanent and devastating effects on the human body when ingested. Would you willingly eat unknown bacteria and fungus?

7   Scientists are unable to explain exactly what happens when those elements enter the human body. No studies have been made on the effects of modified foods. To make matters worse, scientists can introduce genes from totally unrelated species. They might add a nut gene into a corn plant or a fish gene into a soybean. In theory, the new gene will improve the original plant. However, it could also introduce new allergens to people who are already dangerously allergic. Scientists assume there will be no long-range problems. They have made this assumption about drugs and pesticides in the past. And they have been proven devastatingly wrong. For example, a common pesticide used after World War II caused deadly problems for people and the environment.

8   Genetically modified seed development is profit driven. The prices for genetically modified seeds are high. The costs would be unbearable for farmers in developing countries. The "eliminate world hunger" argument is a public relations device. It has little reality for people who have no access to the **enhanced** seeds. Furthermore, producing huge amounts of modified food plants would end the need for those food imports. Stopping imports of foods from other countries could harm the economies of those countries that rely on the sales.

9   The problems with genetically altered crops cannot be ignored. Genetic modification is unnatural. Scientists should not hurry a plant's natural growth or how much food it yields. They should not mix unrelated genes. Nature does not add a salmon gene to strawberry seeds. Yet, grocery stores are filled with products containing genetically modified ingredients. Consumers are usually unaware of the way food has been strangely modified. Biotechnology firms have developed and sold modified seeds too quickly. Testing, research, and public discussion have been limited, if they occurred at all.

USING LANGUAGE CA-CCSS: ELD.PI.9-10.6.c.Ex

Read each sentence from the text. Use a dictionary to find the correct definition of the boldfaced word. Then complete the chart by writing the corresponding letter for each definition into the second column.

Definition Options	
A	destructive insects or other animals that attack plants
B	substances that cause a person's body to have an abnormal reaction, such as a rash
C	the total amount of an agricultural product
D	a part of a cell that controls or influences the behavior, appearance, or development of plant or animal and is passed on from its parents
E	very small living things that often cause disease
F	the science of changing living things to produce something useful, such as crops that have added vitamins

Technical and Domain-specific Word	Definition
"Genetically modified crops are more resistant to diseases and **pests**."	
"Generations of plant breeding have improved taste, size, and **yields** of different foods."	
"Genetic modification introduces other elements to the DNA of plants, including **bacteria** and fungus."	
"They might add a nut **gene** into a corn plant or a fish gene into a soybean."	
"**Biotechnology** firms have developed and sold modified seeds too quickly."	
"However, it could also introduce new **allergens** to people who are already dangerously allergic."	

Please note that excerpts and passages in the StudySync® library and this workbook are intended as touchstones to generate interest in an author's work. The excerpts and passages do not substitute for the reading of entire texts, and StudySync® strongly recommends that students seek out and purchase the whole literary or informational work in order to experience it as the author intended. Links to online resellers are available in our digital library. In addition, complete works may be ordered through an authorized reseller by filling out and returning to StudySync® the order form enclosed in this workbook.

Reading & Writing Companion   79

MEANINGFUL INTERACTIONS CA-CCSS: ELD.PI.9-10.1.Ex ,ELD.PI.9-10.6.a.Ex

According to the text, in which ways can crops be genetically modified? Focus your discussion on paragraphs 1 and 3 in the Point essay and paragraphs 1 and 2 in the Counterpoint essay. Use the speaking frames below to share ways that crops are changed genetically. Remember to paraphrase key ideas from the text. Use the self-assessment rubric to evaluate your participation in the discussion.

Point Paragraphs 1 and 3

- Crops can be modified in many ways. For example, . . .

- The Point author says farmers like modified crops because . . .

- Other ways crops are modified are . . .

Counterpoint Paragraphs 1 and 2

- The Counterpoint author thinks that modifying crops causes . . .

- Another reason the Counterpoint author says modifying crops is bad is . . .

- In my own words, I think . . .

 ## SELF-ASSESSMENT RUBRIC CA-CCSS: ELD.PI.9-10.1.Ex

	4 I did this well.	**3** I did this pretty well.	**2** I did this a little bit.	**1** I did not do this.
I expressed my comments clearly.				
I supported my comments using evidence from the text.				
I paraphrased the key ideas in the text correctly.				
I took turns sharing my comments with the group.				

REREAD

Reread the Point paragraphs of "The Science of Genetically Altering Foods: Should We Do It?" After you reread, complete the Using Language and Meaningful Interactions activities.

USING LANGUAGE   CA-CCSS: ELD.PII.9-10.2.b.Ex

Read each sentence. Choose the correct connecting word to complete each sentence.

1. That resistance is appealing to farmers _____ insects cause huge crop losses every year.

   ○ because   ○ so

2. Farmers have to use a lot of pesticides to protect their crops. _____, genetically modified plants would most likely need only one application of a pesticide.

   ○ However   ○ Then

3. Farmers save time and money. _____, not reapplying pesticides will help the environment.

   ○ In addition   ○ Because

4. One reason for this increased demand is that genetically modified corn, cotton, and soybean seeds have larger crop yields. The plants can _____ be modified to improve nutrition.

   ○ also   ○ however

5. Plants and animals have been modified throughout history with the help of science. _____, with crossbreeding, a single mustard species developed into broccoli, Brussels sprouts, and cabbage.

   ○ First   ○ For example

6. Generations of plant breeding have improved taste, size, and yields of different foods. Those changes take time. _____, genetic modification can change seeds in one generation.

   ○ For example   ○ On the other hand

7. The seeds may be expensive, _____ farmers save on fewer pesticides.

   ○ or   ○ but

8. Farmers can grow larger, disease-resistant crops. _____, more crops will eliminate world hunger.

   ○ Finally   ○ First

MEANINGFUL INTERACTIONS   CA-CCSS: ELD.PI.9-10.1.Ex

The Point author makes the claim that genetically modified crops are a good thing. What are some reasons that the author gives to support this claim? Do the reasons that the author gives support the claim effectively? Share your ideas with your small group. Remember to follow the turn-taking rules. Then, use the self-assessment rubric to evaluate your participation in the discussion.

- The main claim that the Point author makes is . . .

- One reason the Point author gives to support the claim is . . .

- Other reasons the Point author gives to support the claim are . . . and . . .

- I think the Point author is/is not effective in supporting the idea that genetically modified crops are a good thing because . . .

SELF-ASSESSMENT RUBRIC   CA-CCSS: ELD.PI.9-10.1.Ex

	4 I did this well.	3 I did this pretty well.	2 I did this a little bit.	1 I did not do this.
I expressed my ideas clearly.				
I used the text for gathering the reasons that the author gave for supporting the Point claim.				
I explained how well I thought the Point author supported his or her claim about genetically modified crops.				
I took turns sharing my ideas with the group.				

REREAD

Reread the Counterpoint paragraphs of "The Science of Genetically Altering Foods: Should We Do It?" After you reread, complete the Using Language and Meaningful Interactions activities.

USING LANGUAGE CA-CCSS: ELD.PI.9-10.12.b.Ex

Choose the word that correctly completes the sentence. Remember that an affix can change the meaning, form, and sometimes the spelling of a word. The guide below shows the prefix and suffixes used.

Affixes
-ly: suffix that means "like or in the manner of"; turns a noun into an adjective and turns an adjective into an adverb
un- or *in-*: prefix that means "not" or "opposite of"; suffix does not change the form of the word
-ic: suffix that means "having the characteristics of"; changes a noun to an adjective
-ous: suffix that means "full of"; turns the word into an adjective
-al: suffix meaning "relating to"; turns the word into an adjective

1. Most people are already _____ allergic to some foods.

   ○ unserious   ○ seriously

2. Some people who don't agree with genetic modification think that modifying plants is _____.

   ○ unnatural   ○ naturally

3. Scientists can't explain _____ what happens when new elements introduced to the DNA of a plant enter the human body.

   ○ exactly   ○ inexact

4. _____ modification is an issue that people debate.

   ○ Genetically   ○ Genetic

5. Would you _____ eat a plant that had been modified?

   ○ willingly   ○ unwilling

6. People _____ want to eat foods that are safe to consume.

   ○ naturally   ○ unnatural

7. Some people are _____ to eat foods that have been genetically modified.

   ○ unwilling   ○ willingly

8. The Counterpoint author believes scientists should not add a salmon gene to a strawberry seed because the two foods have _____ genes.

   ○ relatedly   ○ unrelated

9. Shoppers who might think all food is grown naturally are _____ not aware of how the food was modified.

   ○ usually   ○ unusual

Please note that excerpts and passages in the StudySync® library and this workbook are intended as touchstones to generate interest in an author's work. The excerpts and passages do not substitute for the reading of entire texts, and StudySync® strongly recommends that students seek out and purchase the whole literary or informational work in order to experience it as the author intended. Links to online resellers are available in our digital library. In addition, complete works may be ordered through an authorized reseller by filling out and returning to StudySync® the order form enclosed in this workbook.

Reading & Writing Companion   **83**

MEANINGFUL INTERACTIONS CA-CCSS: ELD.PI.9-10.1.Ex, ELD.PI.9-10.11.a.Ex

Should people continue to genetically modify crops, or should this practice be abandoned? Use the speaking frames below to help support your answer. Be sure to offer well-articulated comments supported by textual evidence.

Ask yourself: *Have I thought through what I want to say? Does what I want to say make sense? Could I express myself any more clearly?*

- I think that crops should / should not be genetically modified because . . .

- I think that the Point / Counterpoint author makes a good point when stating . . . because . . .

- I also agree with the idea that . . .

- I can further support my opinion with evidence from the text such as . . .

- I have seen / heard about genetically modified foods, and I think . . .

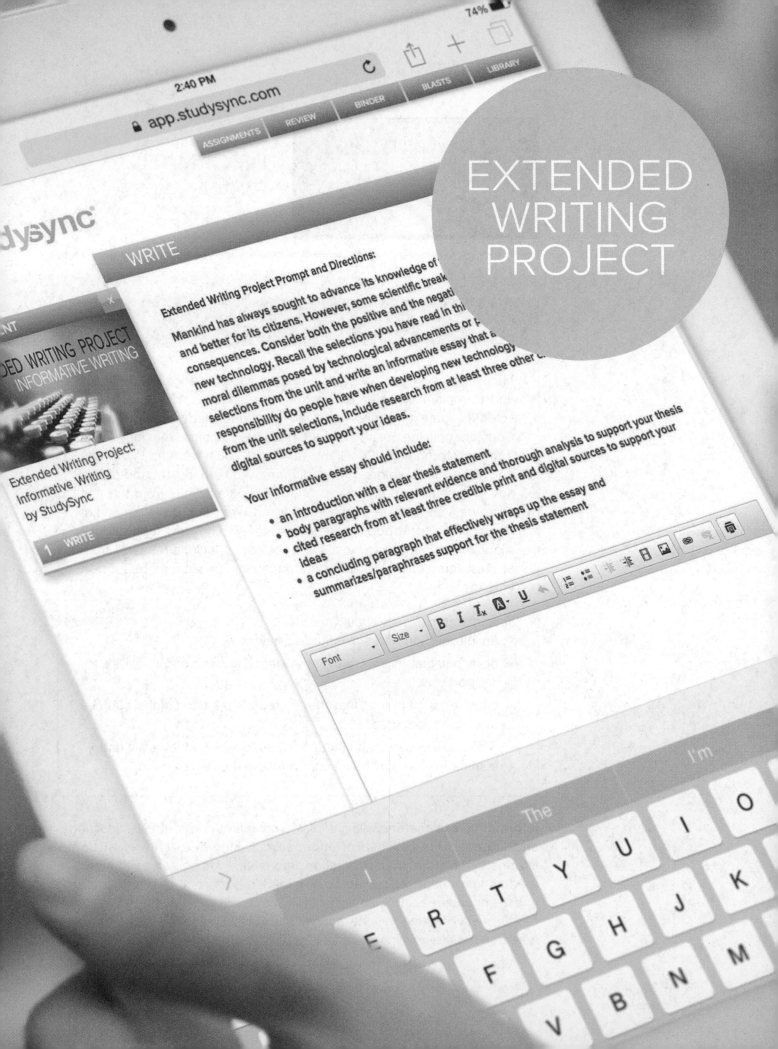

EXTENDED WRITING PROJECT

WRITE

Extended Writing Project Prompt and Directions:

Mankind has always sought to advance its knowledge of and better for its citizens. However, some scientific break consequences. Consider both the positive and the negati new technology. Recall the selections you have read in thi moral dilemmas posed by technological advancements or responsibility do people have when developing new technology selections from the unit and write an informative essay that from the unit selections, include research from at least three other digital sources to support your ideas.

Your informative essay should include:

- an introduction with a clear thesis statement
- body paragraphs with relevant evidence and thorough analysis to support your thesis
- cited research from at least three credible print and digital sources to support your ideas
- a concluding paragraph that effectively wraps up the essay and summarizes/paraphrases support for the thesis statement

Extended Writing Project: Informative Writing by StudySync

NOTES

INFORMATIVE/ EXPLANATORY WRITING

EXTENDED WRITING PROJECT
INFORMATIVE WRITING

WRITING PROMPT

Mankind has always sought to advance its knowledge of the world and to make life easier and better for its citizens. However, some scientific breakthroughs have led to unintended consequences. Consider both the positive and the negative outcomes that may result from new technology. Recall the selections you have read in this unit and how they explore moral dilemmas posed by technological advancements or possibilities. Choose two selections from the unit and write an informative essay that answers this question: What responsibility do people have when developing new technology? Along with information from the unit selections, include research from at least three other credible print and/or digital sources to support your ideas.

Your informative essay should include:
- an introduction with a clear thesis statement
- body paragraphs with relevant evidence and thorough analysis to support your thesis
- cited research from at least three credible print and digital sources to support your ideas
- a concluding paragraph that effectively wraps up the essay and summarizes/paraphrases support for the thesis statement

Informative/explanatory writing explains, compares and contrasts, describes, and informs. One purpose of informative writing is to convey accurate information to the reader. In addition, informative writing serves to increase readers' knowledge of a subject, to help readers better understand processes, and to enhance readers' comprehension of a certain concept. Some examples of informative writing include analytical essays, scientific studies, reports, research papers, newspaper articles, and other non-fiction texts.

Copyright © Bookheaded Learning, LLC

Strong informative writing introduces a main idea, often in the form of a thesis statement. The writing then develops that main idea with supporting details. Information, ideas, and concepts are organized so that each new element builds on what preceded it, to create a piece that is unified and whole. The writing stays focused on the main idea, using transition words to help create flow and make clear connections between supporting details. Although informative writing draws a conclusion to support the thesis, the writing is always objective, unbiased, and free of opinion.

Finally, informative writing incorporates strong, accurate outside research to help make and support ideas and claims. Outside research is a valuable writing element that is essential to the development of a topic. Research enables writers to not only discover and confirm facts, but to draw new conclusions. Sources used in research must be formally cited—that is, referenced and identified using specific guidelines.

Main features of informative/explanatory writing include:

- a clear and logical organizational structure
- an introduction with a clear thesis statement
- relevant facts, supporting details, and quotations used to develop the topic
- information from research sources with formal citations
- precise language and domain-specific vocabulary
- a concluding statement that supports the thesis, information, and topic

In order to present these features accurately and engagingly as they write their essays, students must pay careful attention to:

- a formal style and objective tone
- logical and varied transitions to connect ideas

As you continue with this extended writing project, you will receive more instructions and practice to help you craft each of the elements of informative/ explanatory writing in your own essay. You will also learn more about incorporating research into your essays to make and support ideas and claims. The Student Model for this lesson incorporates one method for citing sources; you will learn more about this method as well as others in a later lesson.

 ## STUDENT MODEL

Before you get started on your own informative/explanatory essay, begin by reading this essay that one student wrote in response to the writing prompt. As you read the Student Model, highlight and annotate the features of informative/explanatory writing that the student included in the essay.

The Moral Dilemma of Technology: Benefit versus Harm

Technology is often viewed as inherently good. When technology improves the human condition, such as enabling cures for disease, society sees it as a benefit. A moral dilemma arises, however, when negative effects, such as physical or emotional pain, accompany the benefit. Society must then weigh the benefit of the value against its human costs, and an important question must be answered: What responsibility do we have when developing new technology? Louis Pasteur, in his speech "Worship the Spirit of Criticism: Address at the Pasteur Institute," and Rebecca Skloot, in the biography *The Immortal Life of Henrietta Lacks*, address this dilemma and its questions. Each focuses on a shared belief: Society bears a responsibility to ensure that, when developing new technology, it addresses unintended consequences that threaten the sanctity of human life.

In 1888, the Pasteur Institute in Paris—a place where Louis Pasteur and his pupils "could work together for science and the cure of disease"—officially opened (Keim and Lumet 176). In his address upon its opening, Pasteur urged his colleagues and students to scrutinize their work and bear moral responsibility for their research, advising them to "Worship the spirit of criticism...without it, everything is fallible . . ." He added that although science binds itself to no country, a scientist must be aware of "the influence which his works may have in this world." Pasteur felt that awareness applied to science and to its impact on humanity. "Louis Pasteur was a humanist who put himself and science to work to improve the human condition" (Persson 44). In closing his address, Pasteur presented his "philosophic reflections" about scientific advancement and making choices between positive and negative impacts of science (Keim and Lumet 182). "Two contrary laws seem to be wrestling with each other nowadays," Pasteur stated. "[T]he one, a law of blood and death, ever imagining new means of destruction and forcing nations to be constantly ready for the battlefield—the other, a law of peace, work and health, ever evolving new means of delivering man from the scourges which beset him." For Pasteur, the choice between the conflicting laws of science—one that "seeks violent conquests" and destruction in war, and the other that finds "relief of humanity" that "places one human life above any victory"—was clear. He would obey "the law of humanity, to extend the frontiers of life."

Pasteur undeniably saw the conflict surrounding technological advancement of his time. He encouraged taking responsibility for research and its consequences.

Copyright © BookheadEd Learning, LLC

Rebecca Skloot sees a similar conflict over advancing medical technology and an "ethical debate surrounding the use of human tissues in research . . . ." In particular, as Skloot's writing points out, the dilemma she deals with concerns the important medical advancements made through the discovery and use of HeLa cells and, in part, the problems medical advances created for the family of Henrietta Lacks, for whom the cells were named. The problems stemmed from the family's anger over the removal of cells from Henrietta's body without permission after she died, over the sale of vials of the cells for $25 for research, and the publication of articles about the cells without their knowledge. Family members felt that the scientific community had taken advantage of them. In addition, Henrietta's contribution was not properly acknowledged by the scientific community; indeed, early Internet research conducted by Skloot revealed that most sites referred to her as Helen Lane. As background, Skloot tells us that HeLa cells are "said to be 'immortal'" because they were taken from a cancerous tumor that killed Henrietta Lacks and now live on outside her body in culture. She also says that billions of HeLa cells are used in laboratories around the world, and that they helped with some of the most important advances in medicine. She further tells us that only after completing some of her own biological research using HeLa cells, Skloot learned through reading magazine articles of the Lacks family's anger. As a researcher attempting to discover and tell the whole story of Henrietta Lacks, of HeLa cells, and of technological advances using them, Skloot dug deeper into information about the Lacks family and tried to make sense of the history of cell culture and the ethical debate about human tissue research. Ultimately, she became one voice calling for the scientific community to acknowledge the harm done to the Lacks family as medical advancements were made with HeLa cells. Then, another ethical controversy erupted. German researchers published data from a study of the HeLa genome—the complete genetic material present in a line of HeLa cells. It was "data with the potential to reveal some very private information about Ms. Lacks' descendants, including their risks of various diseases" (Collins). Many people joined in the demand for moral responsibility. "After outcries from the Lacks family, scientists, bioethicists, and many others, the HeLa genome sequence was removed from a public database" (Collins). Ultimately, the U.S. National Institutes of Health made amends. An agreement was struck taking into account both the advancement of medical research and the concerns of Lacks' descendants. "In addition, the agreement asks researchers who use or derive genomic data from HeLa cells to acknowledge the contribution of Ms. Lacks and her family in their publications" (Collins).

The works of Pasteur and Skloot illustrate sharp contrasts in how society addresses the consequences of a technological benefit. Two anecdotes—one of Pasteur's approach to research and his human subjects and the other about Skloot's discovery of Henrietta Lacks—further illustrate the contrast in connections, lost or kept, between research and an individual's impact on it. In 1885, "Pasteur tested his pioneering rabies treatment on man for the first time" (Dhoke). The patient was a 9-year-old boy and "The child stood it admirably, but Pasteur became anxious, distressed to the point of sleeplessness, when it came time to pass on the . . . vaccines" (Keim and Lumet 171). "This was done at some personal risk for Pasteur, since he was not a licensed physician and could have faced prosecution for treating the boy. After consulting with colleagues, he decided to go ahead with the treatment." (Wikipedia 1). The vaccine soon became widely used and "Pasteur took an interest in the children who he treated . . . trying to keep watch on their subsequent lives . . ." (Keim and Lumet 175). On the other hand, Skloot tells of asking her high school science teacher for details about Henrietta Lacks. Her teacher's response was "I wish I could tell you . . . but no one knows anything about her."

Although a span of some 120 years separates Pasteur's and Skloot's writings, the common thread binding them is an underlying moral principle: Society has a twofold responsibility in the development of technology. It must ensure that the benefits technology offers to humanity are evaluated in conjunction with its potential unintended, harmful consequences.

Works Cited

Collins, Francis. "HeLa Cells: A New Chapter in An Enduring Story." *National Institutes of Health*. U.S. Department of Health and Human Services. 7 August 2013. Web. 12 August 2015.

Dhoke, Ruchira. "LOUIS PASTEUR: the man who built the foundation for the science of microbiology and modern medicine." *The National*. 20 October 2014. Web. 12 August 2015.

Keim, Albert, and Louis Lumet. *Louis Pasteur*. Trans. Frederic Taber Cooper. New

York: Frederick A. Stokes, 1914. Print.

Pasteur, Louis. "Worship the Spirit of Criticism." *StudySync*. BookheadEd

Learning, LLC., 2015.

Persson, Sheryl. *Smallpox, Syphilis, and Salvation: Medical Breakthroughs that

Changed the World*. Australia: Exisle Publishing, 2010. Print.

Skloot, Rebecca. *The Immortal Life of Henrietta Lacks. StudySync*. BookheadEd

Learning, LLC., 2015. Web. 12 August 2015.

THINK QUESTIONS

1. What is the central idea of the Student Model? Where does the writer introduce the central idea in the essay?

2. How are the writer's ideas developed and refined by sentences, paragraphs, or larger portions of the text?

3. How does the writer sound in this essay? Is her language casual or formal? How does the writer remain objective? Explain.

4. In thinking about the Student Model and writing your own informative essay, what types of sources can you use to respond to the prompt?

5. Based on what you have read, listened to, or researched, how would you answer the question *What responsibility do we have for what we create?* What are some issues associated with this question today?

PREWRITE

CA-CCSS: CA.RI.9-10.1, CA.W.9-10.5, CA.W.9-10.6, CA.W.9-10.9a, CA.W.9-10.9b

WRITING PROMPT

Mankind has always sought to advance its knowledge of the world and to make life easier and better for its citizens. However, some scientific breakthroughs have led to unintended consequences. Consider both the positive and the negative outcomes that may result from new technology. Recall the selections you have read in this unit and how they explore moral dilemmas posed by technological advancements or possibilities. Choose two selections from the unit and write an informative essay that answers this question: What responsibility do people have when developing new technology? Along with information from the unit selections, include research from at least three other credible print and/or digital sources to support your ideas.

Your informative essay should include:

- an introduction with a clear thesis statement

- body paragraphs with relevant evidence and thorough analysis to support your thesis

- cited research from at least three credible print and digital sources to support your ideas

- a concluding paragraph that effectively wraps up the essay and summarizes/paraphrases support for the thesis statement

When beginning the process of writing your informative/explanatory essay, think about strategies you have used in the past to gather and organize your ideas. You likely used one of the following techniques—questioning, brainstorming, list making, creating a word web, outlining, or free writing—to develop your essays

Before you begin your essay, think about specific questions related to the Extended Writing Project prompt to help guide your brainstorming and focus on the topic dictated by the prompt. The prompt encourages you to consider the positive and negative effects of new technology and how the unit texts address moral dilemmas posed by technological advancements or possibilities. It also directs you to explain what responsibility people must assume when developing technology that is intended to benefit humanity. Let's examine what the writer of the Student Model did to prepare to write her essay in response to this prompt.

Texts: "Worship the Spirit of Criticism: Address at the Pasteur Institute" by Louis Pasteur and *The Immortal Life of Henrietta Lacks* by Rebecca Skloot

The writer thought about what she read in "Worship the Spirit of Criticism: Address at the Pasteur Institute" and *The Immortal Life of Henrietta Lacks*. She asked, What moral dilemmas with regard to technology do the texts explore? What benefits and drawbacks to humanity that result from new technology do the texts identify? In each text, what responsibility or lack of responsibility does the scientific community exhibit as a result of its endeavors? She then made a list of the answers to these questions and put them in a chart:

	TEXT 1: "WORSHIP THE SPIRIT OF CRITICISM" BY LOUIS PASTEUR	TEXT 2: *THE IMMORTAL LIFE OF HENRIETTA LACKS* BY REBECCA SKLOOT
What is the technology?	scientific discoveries, particularly in medicine	medical advancements
Who or what is affected by it?	mankind in general	patients and their families
What moral dilemma(s) does each text explore?	What kinds of technology are acceptable to pursue? (only those intended to save and improve lives, as opposed to those intended to destroy or kill?)	How must the scientific community behave toward the individual human beings (and their families) from whom the tissue used in medical research comes?

What benefits to humanity does each text identify?	saving lives and helping people live longer	changing and improving medical science using HeLa cells that lead to important advancements in medicine
What costs to humanity does each text identify?	technology that leads to the destruction of lives	personal, hurtful consequences for Henrietta Lacks's family
What responsibility do people have when developing new technology?	Pasteur holds the scientific community responsible for ensuring that technology benefits rather than harms humanity.	Skloot's discoveries suggest that the scientific community has a responsibility to be open, honest, and respectful toward those individuals and their families who contribute to science through the use of their personal tissue.

- Complete the *Prewriting Mind Map* graphic organizer using two selections from the unit that you believe offer the most insight on the responsibility associated with new technology. As you write down your ideas in the chart, look for patterns that emerge. Do the technological advancements examined have anything in common? In what similar or different ways do the authors of the selections explore moral dilemmas posed by technology? What key benefits and costs to humanity result from the technological advancements mentioned in the two selections? What responsibility do people have when developing new technology according to the two texts? Looking for similarities as well as differences between how the texts treat the subject may help you solidify the ideas you want to discuss in your essay.

- Now brainstorm a list of questions you would like to have answered as you research. Questions might include: What information, such as that found in other sources (research studies, biographical or historical accounts, print or electronic publications), is available on the topic? What do other sources say about technology and its benefits and costs to humanity? Do other authors agree or disagree with the information in the unit selections you chose, and if so, how? What new or additional data or information about a particular technology explored in one of the unit texts is now available? Keep these questions in mind as you research your topic. Other questions may arise as you progress.

Copyright © BookheadEd Learning, LLC

SKILL:
RESEARCH AND
NOTE-TAKING

⭐ DEFINE

Researching is the process of gathering data, such as facts and other information about a topic of interest or importance to you. Research helps writers narrow or broaden their inquiry into a topic, develop a point of view, and draw conclusions by providing relevant evidence and details that support claims. The point of view and conclusions you draw from research help solidify the main idea, or thesis, of a topic. Good research will not only help you formulate ideas, but will also increase your understanding of a topic and strengthen your writing.

Research involves the systematic investigation of general and specific factual information relevant to your research topic from multiple print and digital sources, avoiding overreliance on one source.

When performing research online using a search engine, remember to use accurate keywords and online filters to narrow the results and limit the number of distracting and irrelevant results. Try a variety of words for different searches in order to come up with the widest range of options.

Wikipedia is an extremely popular source of information, but it is not a primary source as it provides summaries of other sources and common knowledge. Although you should avoid using it as source itself for a formal research paper, it can be a helpful tool to jumpstart research. You can look up information on Wikipedia and follow the links to the original sources cited as Wikipedia references.

●●● IDENTIFICATION AND APPLICATION

Before you decide to use a source, consider the following factors to evaluate its credibility:

• **Authority** — Is the source material written by a recognized expert or experts on the topic? Authors who have written several books or articles about a subject for informed audiences in the field and who are frequently quoted may be considered authorities.

- **Reliability** — Has the source material been published in a trustworthy book, periodical, or website? Use materials from scholarly journals or from well-respected magazines and newspapers. Keep in mind that websites of well-known experts, universities, and organizations are more reliable than those of unknown individuals.

- **Objectivity** — Is the source material connected with persons or organizations that are biased? Does it present only a single perspective or point of view? If the person or organization has something to gain by presenting information in a certain way, the source might not be objective. Subjective information is told from only one point of view.

- **Currency** — Is the source material up to date or based on the most current information? In general, use the most recent material available, particularly for subjects of current importance. Check the publication date of books, magazines, and websites. However, depending on the topic, the source material may not need to be current. For example, currency is not an issue in primary source material such as documents and letters and may not be important in secondary source material such as biographies of historical figures.

As you use a source, take a closer look at it. Consider the following questions to evaluate its accuracy:

- **Is the information presented verified by other sources?** If you find conflicting information, check a third or even a fourth source.

- **Is the source itself based on other reliable sources?** This is particularly important with secondary sources. See if the document lists its sources in a bibliography or links to reliable primary sources if it is an online source.

- **Does the document explain how the information was gathered or obtained?** You might want to determine whether the author did a thorough research job or only a quick study. You might want to know whether the author used only the Internet for research or also used special libraries and museum holdings. Sometimes the preface of the book or article will tell you this.

An essential part of the research process is note-taking. **Note-taking** is a process, or consistent and systematic way, of writing down select pieces of information, either in your own words or as direct quotes taken from a source. Notes will help you develop or support a topic about which you are writing. Information you choose for your notes should strongly support your topic and answer questions you encounter while researching. Good notes can help you keep your topic focused, make connections between ideas, and become evidence you cite to support or broaden ideas. Since notes help you keep track of information, they need to be organized and document not only

NOTES

information you are going to use, but also tell where, from whom, and when you found the information. Documenting information will help you track it down later if you need to find it again as you are writing.

When researching and taking notes, you need to choose the method, or combination of methods, that works best for you. Think about what you have learned from research presentations you prepared for previous units or have been working on in the current unit. Consider what worked well for keeping your information organized and systematic. Here are some methods used by researchers when taking notes:

- **Note cards** with information written on standard 3×5", 4×6", or 5×8" index cards:
  - › **Source cards** are note cards that document the author (Last name first), title of an article or book, publication information, and location where the source can be found, such as a library or the Internet. Include URLs (Uniform Resource Locators) or reference addresses for information found on the Internet. It is a good idea to number each source card.
  - › **Note cards** include key words, phrases, direct quotations or paraphrased quotations, and summaries that specifically relate to the topic. The information on the cards should be relatively short and to the point. Use a new card for each piece of information you want to consider or use. You can **quote** the exact words of an author or expert by enclosing all the borrowed words in quotation marks to make it clear that the ideas belong to someone else. You can also also **paraphrase,** that is, restate the researched information, in your own words, although you still need to cite the original source of the information. Through experience, you can develop a good sense of when it is more effective to quote or to paraphrase researched information. Sometimes quoting is better because the actual wording is especially interesting or comes from an important source. Other times, it is more elegant to pull out a few key words or phrases from the source and integrate them into the flow of original writing. For longer pieces of work, such as chapters or sections, you can **summarize** main ideas in your own words. Note cards should include the source and a page number, or paragraph number, where the information can be found. If you use the system of numbering source cards, write the number of the source card related to the piece of information you are considering using on the note card where you can find it easily.
  - › **Online note cards** help some researchers organize, document, and print the information they find. There are a variety of sources that sell computer programs for creating cards or some that offer access to online systems or programs that compile and organize information. Online systems often require the user to set up an account. Consumers

Please note that excerpts and passages in the StudySync® library and this workbook are intended as touchstones to generate interest in an author's work. The excerpts and passages do not substitute for the reading of entire texts, and StudySync® strongly recommends that students seek out and purchase the whole literary or informational work in order to experience it as the author intended. Links to online resellers are available in our digital library. In addition, complete works may be ordered through an authorized reseller by filling out and returning to StudySync® the order form enclosed in this workbook.

Reading & Writing Companion

97

NOTES

of online products need to weigh the benefits, such as saving time writing and organizing, against difficulty or ease of use and cost.

- **Notebooks**—physical or electronic—are another way writers keep track of their notes. Notes in a notebook should include the same information as those on note cards.

- **Bibliographic information lists** are another way some researchers keep track of sources. They create computer-generated lists of bibliographic information to help document and organize their source material. Bibliographic information is the same as the information included on a source card.

Regardless of which methods you choose, you must always avoid **plagiarizing,** or taking another person's work and passing it off as your own, whether intentionally or not. If the notes you take from a source and information you use is accurate and attributed to the source on your note cards, you will avoid plagiarizing anyone's work when you are writing. There are specific, formal guidelines for writing research papers and including source information that you should learn to use. You will learn more about how to do this in the Sources and Citations lesson.

No matter the subject, any time you are writing an informational/explanatory essay, you can use the following roadmap to help you as you research your topic. This roadmap will help you to focus on important ideas as well as guide you toward the kind of information you'll want to include in your essay:

- Create a web or diagram of ideas and facts pertaining to your chosen subject; use the information to help you think of relevant issues or questions regarding your subject.

- Find sources and references that support and explain your subject; read general and specific information in books as well as magazine and newspaper articles in print and on the Internet. You might also look to video, poetry, songs, or artwork that would help to validate or authenticate your focus. Find information that is relevant to your topic and audience. Be mindful of what sources are considered valid or not valid.

- Make a bibliographic list of references.

- Read information in sources and make cards for sources and references.

- Create note cards with quotes, paraphrases, or summaries of information.

 MODEL

Here is the roadmap the author used in researching and taking notes to develop the second paragraph of the essay. While the writer could have used a graphic organizer to guide her organization, she chose to use an outline of questions to answer:

Student Outline for Paragraph Two

Main Idea: What were Pasteur's beliefs about advancements in science and technology? What were his beliefs about taking responsibility for them?

A. Where, when, why did Pasteur present his ideas and beliefs in a speech?

B. What did Pasteur believe? What responsibility do scientists have . . . ?

   1. For evaluating their work

   2. As scientists in general

C. What kind of person was Pasteur in the context of science?

D. What philosophical beliefs did Pasteur have about advancements in science and technology?

   1. Beneficial

   2. Harmful

E. What did Pasteur believe was the right way to develop or advance science and technology?

As the student read from Pasteur's speech and other sources to find answers to her questions, she made a list of sources to use for Paragraph 2.

Works Cited

Keim, Albert, and Louis Lumet. *Louis Pasteur.* Trans. Frederic Taber Cooper. New

   York: Frederick A. Stokes, 1914. Print.

Pasteur, Louis. "Worship the Spirit of Criticism." *StudySync.* BookheadEd

   Learning, LLC., 2015. Web. 12 August 2015.

Persson, Sheryl. *Smallpox, Syphilis, and Salvation: Medical Breakthroughs that*

   Changed the World. Australia: Exisle Publishing, 2010. Print.

Then the writer made source cards with information about the sources and numbered them.

NOTES

Sample Source Cards

(Source) (source number) 1	(Source) (source number) 2
Keim, Albert, and Louis Lumet. <u>Louis Pasteur</u>. Trans. Frederic Taber Cooper. New York: Frederick A. Stokes, 1914. Print. (Where to find it) Public School or Library (Library call number)	Pasteur, Louis. "Worship the Spirit of Criticism." *StudySync*. BookheadEd Learning, LLC., 2015. Web. 12 August 2015. (Where to find it) Internet: list URL address
(Source) (source number) 3	
Persson, Sheryl. <u>Smallpox, Syphilis, and Salvation: Medical Breakthroughs that Changed the World.</u> Australia: Exisle Publishing, 2010. Print. (Where to find it) Public School or Library (Library call number)	

Next, she made note cards with information she wanted to use that helped answer her questions.

Sample Note Cards

(Key Words) (source number) 1 **Where, when, why did Pasteur present his ideas in a speech?** (Information, details, or quote) In 1888, the Pasteur Institute in Paris—a place where Louis Pasteur and his pupils "could work together for science and the cure of disease" —officially opened. (Keim and Lumet p. 176)	(Key Words) (source number) 2 **What did Pasteur believe? What responsibility do scientists have for evaluating their work?** (Information, details, or quote) "Worship the spirit of criticism . . .without it, everything is fallible . . ." (Pasteur speech)
(Key Words) (Source number) 3 **What did Pasteur believe? What responsibility do scientists have in general?** (Information, details, or quote) (paraphrase) although science binds itself to no country, a scientist must be aware of (quote) "the influence that his work may have in this world" (Pasteur speech)	(Key Words) (source number) 4 **What kind of person was Pasteur in the context of science?** (Information, details, or quote) "Louis Pasteur was a humanist who put himself and science to work to improve the human condition" (Persson p. 44)

After taking notes and completing her research, the author began to write the second paragraph of her essay. Here is what she wrote:

*In 1888, the Pasteur Institute in Paris—a place where Louis Pasteur and his pupils **"could work together for science and the cure of disease"**—officially opened (Keim and Lumet 176). In his address upon its opening, Pasteur urged his colleagues and students to scrutinize their work and bear moral responsibility for their research, advising them to **"Worship the spirit of***

NOTES

criticism . . . without it, everything is fallible . . ." He added that although science binds itself to no country, a scientist must be aware of **"the influence that his work may have in this world."** Pasteur felt that awareness applied to science and to its impact on humanity. **"Louis Pasteur was a humanist who put himself and science to work to improve the human condition"** (Persson 44).

Notice that her essay contains citations in parentheses for her sources and the page numbers where the information is found. These citations follow MLA style, although other style guides may dictate the use of footnotes or endnotes. The Sources and Citations lesson will provide more detailed information about how to accurately cite sources both within the body of the text and in a Works Cited page that follows it.

 ## PRACTICE

Create four note cards that properly record quoted or paraphrased information from your sources. When you are finished, trade with a partner and offer each other feedback. Do the cards contain all of the necessary source information? Do direct quotes appear in quotations? Do the notes address the writer's questions? Offer each other suggestions, and remember that they are most helpful when they are constructive.

SKILL:
THESIS
STATEMENT

DEFINE

The thesis statement is one of the most important elements in an informative/ explanatory essay. It introduces what the writer is going to say about the topic of the essay, helps control and focus the information the writer provides, and summarizes the central or main idea. It also gives the reader an overview of the ideas the writer will develop in the body of the essay. Ideas presented in a good thesis statement, although somewhat general, must also be focused on, or specific to, the topic. Words used in the thesis statement should narrow the focus of the topic without too many details. For example, a thesis statement that says, "drugs are bad," is too broad and vague. It could be strengthened by a more specific focus by stating what kinds of drugs are bad, for whom they are bad, and why. The details about the topic will come later in the body of the essay as the writer develops his or her central idea. The thesis statement usually appears near the end of the essay's introductory paragraph. The rest of the paragraphs in the essay all support the thesis statement with facts, evidence, and examples.

IDENTIFICATION AND APPLICATION

A thesis statement:

- is a short, focused statement that makes a strong, clear assertion identifying and previewing the writer's central idea

- lets the reader know the direction the writer will take in the body of the essay, especially what the writer plans to discuss, support, or prove

- is presented in the introductory paragraph, usually near the end

- helps the writer focus on relationships among pieces of evidence from multiple sources used to support ideas, arguments, or conclusions

- responds fully, or completely, and specifically to an essay prompt

MODEL

The following is the introductory paragraph from the Student Model essay "The Moral Dilemma of Technology: Benefit versus Harm":

> Technology is often viewed as inherently good. When technology improves the human condition, such as enabling cures for disease, society sees it as a benefit. A moral dilemma arises, however, when negative effects, such as physical or emotional pain, accompany the benefit. Society must then weigh the benefit of the value against its human costs, and an important question must be answered: What responsibility do we have when developing new technology? Louis Pasteur, in his speech "Worship the Spirit of Criticism: Address at the Pasteur Institute," and Rebecca Skloot, in the biography *The Immortal Life of Henrietta Lacks*, address this dilemma and its questions. Each focuses on a shared belief: **Society bears a responsibility to ensure that, when developing new technology, it addresses unintended consequences that threaten the sanctity of human life.**

Notice the bold-faced thesis statement at the end of the introductory paragraph. This student's thesis statement asserts the writer's central or main idea about that topic: that society must take responsibility for addressing unintended consequences of technology. It appears at the end of the introductory paragraph, after the writer has introduced her topic (the moral dilemma posed by technology that offers benefits but also involves negative consequences). Notice how the writer also identifies the two unit texts she will analyze in the essay (Louis Pasteur's "Worship the Spirit of Criticism: Address at the Pasteur Institute" and Rebecca Skloot's *The Immortal Life of Henrietta Lacks*). In this way, she provides readers with the appropriate context for her thesis and specifically addresses the essay prompt, which is "Choose two selections from the unit and write an informative essay that answers this question: What responsibility do people have when developing new technology?"

PRACTICE

Write a thesis statement for your informative essay that articulates your central idea in relation to the essay prompt. When you are finished, trade with a partner and offer each other feedback. How clear was the writer's central idea? Is it obvious what this essay will focus on? Does it specifically address the prompt? Offer each other suggestions, and remember that they are most helpful when they are constructive.

SKILL:
ORGANIZE
INFORMATIVE
WRITING

 DEFINE

The purpose of writing an informative/explanatory text is to inform readers. To do this effectively, writers need to organize and present their ideas, facts, details, and other information in a logical sequence that is easy to understand.

Students are often asked to write informative essays as part of their studies in English language arts classes. A common method for writing a strong informative essay is organizing the writing using the **five-paragraph strategy.** As you saw in the introductory lesson, this consists of an **introductory paragraph** that presents the **topic** and the writer's position in a **thesis statement**. The introduction is then followed by **three body paragraphs**, each of which presents evidentiary details and ideas that support some aspect of the essay's thesis. The fifth paragraph is a **conclusion** that provides a unique restatement of the thesis, reviews the evidence presented, and ends with a concluding sentence that wraps up the topic. The five-paragraph approach is straightforward, concise, and effective; however, it is not the only organizational structure that may be used to write a strong informative essay.

Experienced writers carefully choose an **organizational structure** that best suits their material. They often use an outline or other graphic organizer to determine which organizational structure will help them express their ideas most effectively.

For example, scientific reports and studies often use a **cause and effect** structure. This mirrors the information scientists need to relay—the experiment and the results of the experiment. Historians and memoirists often use a **sequential** or a chronological structure, discussing events in the order they occurred. Topical essays by historians may use a **problem and solution** structure in which a social or historical problem such as the Great Depression is presented and is followed by a discussion of how the problem was solved.

A common organizational structure for informative writing involves using a **comparison and contrast** strategy. There are several ways this strategy may be implemented. The writer might focus on one idea or example after the introductory paragraph and then a second idea or example in the subsequent paragraph. Another technique is to compare and contrast related ideas within each paragraph. Sometimes, the writer might choose to mix-and-match the approaches for a more complex structure. In this case, the first section might be dedicated to similarities, but the writer might feel the need to have two paragraphs within this section, one dedicated to each text. The reader would then expect a similar substructure in the second section, with each text being given one paragraph as differences are explained and analyzed.

It is important to remember that while an informative essay or a paragraph may use an overall organizational method, it may be necessary to introduce another organizational technique to convey an important point.

IDENTIFICATION AND APPLICATION

- When selecting an organizational structure, writers must consider the purpose of their writing. They often ask themselves questions about the kind of information they are writing about. Questions they might consider are:
  › "What organizational structure does the language of the prompt suggest?"
  › "What is the main idea I'd like to convey?"
  › "Would it make sense to relay events in the order they occurred?"
  › "What is the problem?"
  › "What solutions seem like possible answers to the problem?"
  › "Is there a natural cause-and-effect relationship in my information?"
  › "Can I compare and contrast different examples of my thesis statement?"
  › "Am I teaching readers how to do something?"

- Writers often use word choice to create connections between details and hint at the organizational structure being used:
  › Sequential order: *first, next, then, finally, last, initially, ultimately*
  › Cause and effect: *because, accordingly, therefore, as a result, effect, so*
  › Compare and contrast: *like, unlike, also, both, similarly, although, while, but, however*

- Sometimes, within the overall structure, writers may find it necessary to organize individual paragraphs using other substructures—a cause-and-effect paragraph in a chronological structure, for instance. This should not affect the overall organization.

- Writers sometimes use headings to organize their ideas and to signal to readers what a particular paragraph or section will focus on.

MODEL

The writer of the Student Model understood—from the prompt itself, which calls upon students to examine two texts, and from her prewriting—that her overall organizational plan should focus on comparing and contrasting examples of how the scientific community responds to unintended consequences of technology.

In this excerpt from the introduction of the Student Model, the writer makes the organizational structure clear with her word choice:

> *Each [selection] focuses on a shared belief:* Society bears a responsibility
> to ensure that, when new developing technology, it addresses unintended
> consequences that threaten the sanctity of human life.

The writer uses the clause "Each [selection] focuses on a shared belief" to make clear that she will show how the two writers—Pasteur and Skloot—explore both the positive and negative effects of technological advancement in science, specifically medicine.

In order to organize her ideas during the prewriting process, the writer used a three-column chart like the one shown below. In the first column, she listed key questions related to her topic: What moral dilemma(s) does each text explore? What benefits to humanity does each text identify? What costs to humanity does each text identify? What responsibility do people have when developing new technology? In the next two columns, she listed the response to each question that she found in the selections by Pasteur and Skloot. She then added comments to her prewriting notes about the similarities and differences between these two authors' points of view and highlighted them in yellow.

	TEXT 1: "WORSHIP THE SPIRIT OF CRITICISM" BY LOUIS PASTEUR	TEXT 2: *THE IMMORTAL LIFE OF HENRIETTA LACKS* BY REBECCA SKLOOT
What is the technology?	scientific discoveries, particularly in medicine	medical advancements
Who or what is affected by it?	mankind in general	patients and their families

NOTES

What moral dilemma(s) does each text explore?	What kinds of technology are acceptable to pursue? (only those intended to save and improve lives, as opposed to those intended to destroy or kill?) Comment: Similar to Skloot, but this is a very broad concern	How must the scientific community behave toward the individual human beings (and their families) from whom the tissue used in medical research comes? Comment: Similar to Pasteur, but this is a very specific concern
What benefits to humanity does each text identify?	saving lives and helping people live longer Comment: Similar to Skloot, but this is broader concern	changing and improving medical science using HeLa cells that lead to important advancements in medicine Comment: Similar to Pasteur, but this is narrower concern
What costs to humanity does each text identify?	technology that leads to the destruction of lives Comment: Very broad concern	personal, hurtful consequences for Henrietta Lacks's family Comment: Very specific concern
What responsibility do people have when developing new technology?	Pasteur holds the scientific community responsible for ensuring that technology benefits rather than harms humanity. Comment: Similar concern as Skloot	Skloot's discoveries suggest that the scientific community has a responsibility to ensure that individuals (and their families) are not harmed in the process of advancing medicine. Comment: Similar concern as Pasteur

PRACTICE

Using the *Organize Informative/Explanatory Writing* graphic organizer like the one you have just examined or another type of graphic organizer, fill in the information you gathered in the Prewrite stage of writing your essay. Add any additional questions that have come up as you analyzed your sources and conducted additional research. Then, as in the Model, comment on similarities and differences between the ways the two texts address each of the questions. Ask yourself: does the information I have gathered lend itself to a compare-and-contrast organizational structure, or would some other structure, such as cause-and-effect or problem-and-solution, work better?

SKILL: SUPPORTING DETAILS

 DEFINE

In informative writing, writers develop their main idea with relevant information called **supporting details.** These details can be drawn both from unit texts as well as from outside research, which helps writers formulate their ideas and provides support for their thesis statements and main points. Relevant information includes all of the following:

- Facts and concrete details relevant to understanding the topic drawn from reliable sources
- Inferences drawn from texts that are important to understanding the topic
- Research and statistics related to the main idea or thesis
- Quotations and anecdotes from experts, eyewitnesses, or other source material
- Conclusions of scientific findings and studies
- Definitions from reference material

Writers can choose supporting details from many sources, including encyclopedias, research papers, newspaper and magazine articles, graphs, memoirs, biographies, criticism, documentaries, and reliable online reference materials. Although information is plentiful and the source material varied, the writer must be careful to evaluate the quality of information to determine what information is most important and most closely related to the thesis. If the information does not support the topic, does not strengthen the writer's point, or is not appropriate to the audience's knowledge of the topic, it is not relevant.

IDENTIFICATION AND APPLICATION

Step 1:

Review your thesis statement. To identify relevant supporting details, ask these questions: What do I want my audience to know about the topic? What is my main idea? Is my thesis statement clear and concrete, *not* vague or abstract? Consider the following sample thesis statement about the Internet:

> Although global information available on the Internet is a valuable resource, **individual users are responsible for ensuring that materials accessed or posted are true, do not invade the privacy of others, and do not cause personal harm.**

The writer wants readers to know that the Internet is a resource that must be used carefully. The writer's main idea is that "individual users are responsible for ensuring that materials accessed or posted are true, do not invade the privacy of others, and do not cause personal harm." This thesis statement is clear and specific.

Step 2:

Ask what a reader needs to know about the topic in order to understand the main idea. What details will support your thesis? Consider the details in this sample body paragraph, which follows the thesis statement:

> A first step in taking responsibility for what you might use or cite from the Internet is to know the reliability of your sources. The Internet is an unregulated resource. People can post information that is both true and false. There are no universal filters required to prove that information is factual.

In order to understand the thesis statement, which includes three responsibilities individual Internet users have, readers will need more information about what each responsibility entails. The second body paragraph explains reasons why users cannot assume that all Internet material is true. This information, which is accurate and concise, relates to the overall purpose of the text and supports the writer's thesis.

Step 3:

Look for facts, quotations, research, and the conclusions of others as evidence for your points and support for your thesis. Consider the sample supporting details that follow the reasons described above:

Please note that excerpts and passages in the StudySync® library and this workbook are intended as touchstones to generate interest in an author's work. The excerpts and passages do not substitute for the reading of entire texts, and StudySync® strongly recommends that students seek out and purchase the whole literary or informational work in order to experience it as the author intended. Links to online resellers are available in our digital library. In addition, complete works may be ordered through an authorized reseller by filling out and returning to StudySync® the order form enclosed in this workbook.

Reading & Writing Companion

111

In fact, some recent studies indicate that between 10% and 50% of information posted on the Internet is unreliable. One rule of thumb for increasing the likelihood that the information you access and use is accurate and reliable is to check the domain name extension of the source. Some of the more reliable sources use .edu, .gov, and sometimes .org within their domain names.

As evidence for his or her point that not all information on the Internet is true, the writer provides a statistic. Now that readers have a better understanding of why the information on the Internet cannot always be trusted, the writer provides a useful tip for how to increase the likelihood that the information Internet users access is reliable.

Note that writers may also include graphics, such as figures and tables, as well as multimedia, such as photographs and video links, in order to support their ideas.

Use the following reader/writer checklists when assessing your essay's supporting details:

- Ask questions to determine if the readers' needs are met:
  › Is the information relevant to the audience?
  › Do the details hold the audience's interest with elements such as facts, statistics, quotations, and anecdotes?
  › Are the details and the language used clear and understandable?
  › Is this information necessary to the reader's understanding of the topic?

- Ask questions to determine if the writer's goals and needs are met:
  › Are the details relevant to the writer's goal?
  › Does the information prove the writer's point or achieve the writer's goal?
  › Is any information weak or should it be replaced with stronger evidence that makes the same point?
  › Are connections made between ideas, and are these connections supported by details and relevant information?
  › Is information selectively integrated into the text to maintain a logical flow of ideas from the thesis, through the body paragraphs, and finally to the conclusion?

MODEL

In the following excerpt from *Einstein's Letter to the President*—a letter written by Albert Einstein to U.S. President Franklin Delano Roosevelt in 1939—Einstein presents the idea that uranium is a powerful and potentially dangerous energy source that requires watchfulness and possibly quick action by the President and his administration.

> Some recent work by E. Fermi and L. Szilard, which has been communicated to me in manuscript, leads me to expect that the element uranium may be turned into a new and important source of energy in the immediate future. **Certain aspects of the situation which has arisen seem to call for watchfulness and if necessary, quick action on the part of the Administration.** I believe therefore that it is my duty to bring to your attention the following facts and recommendations.
>
> In the course of the last four months it has been made probable through the work of Joliot in France as well as Fermi and Szilard in America—that **it may be possible to set up a nuclear chain reaction in a large mass of uranium, by which vast amounts of power and large quantities of new radium-like elements would be generated.** Now it appears almost certain that this could be achieved in the immediate future.
>
> **This new phenomenon would also lead to the construction of bombs,** and it is conceivable—though much less certain—that extremely powerful bombs of this type may thus be constructed. A single bomb of this type, carried by boat and exploded in a port, might very well destroy the whole port together with some of the surrounding territory. However, such bombs might very well prove too heavy for transportation by air.

In the first paragraph, Einstein alerts President Roosevelt about some new information he has acquired about uranium and its potential. He begins to develop the central idea that uranium requires monitoring and possibly quick action by the government. He is vague about his exact concern and why the government needs to monitor it or take action, but he implies that it is an important matter that warrants the President's attention.

In the second and third paragraphs, Einstein provides additional details and selectively integrates information about the power of uranium and its potentially destructive capability in order to reinforce the central idea that the uranium situation requires governmental action and to heighten the president's sense of urgency. During the course of the three paragraphs, Einstein goes from general to more specific to build connections and create more impact.

NOTES

⚡ PRACTICE

Using the *Supporting Details in Informative/Explanatory Writing* graphic organizer, identify details from the two unit texts you have chosen and from additional research sources you have identified that support your thesis statement, which you should write in the center circle. You may add surrounding circles as necessary. Keep in mind that you will organize these details into a logical structure during the Plan lesson.

NOTES

PLAN

CA-CCSS: CA.W.9-10.2a, CA.W.9-10.2b, CA.W.9-10.4, CA.W.9-10.5, CA.W.9-10.6, CA.W.9-10.9a, CA.W.9-10.9b, CA.SL.9-10.1c

WRITING PROMPT

Mankind has always sought to advance its knowledge of the world and to make life easier and better for its citizens. However, some scientific breakthroughs have led to unintended consequences. Consider both the positive and the negative outcomes that may result from new technology. Recall the selections you have read in this unit and how they explore moral dilemmas posed by technological advancements or possibilities. Choose two selections from the unit and write an informative essay that answers this question: What responsibility do people have when developing new technology? Along with information from the unit selections, include research from at least three other credible print and/or digital sources to support your ideas.

Your informative essay should include:

- an introduction with a clear thesis statement
- body paragraphs with relevant evidence and thorough analysis to support your thesis
- cited research from at least three credible print and digital sources to support your ideas
- a concluding paragraph that effectively wraps up the essay and summarizes/paraphrases support for the thesis statement

Review the information you have collected in your *Organize Informative/ Explanatory Writing* and *Supporting Details in Informative/Explanatory Writing* graphic organizers. This organized information and your thesis will help you to create a road map to use for writing your essay.

Consider the following questions as you develop your main paragraph topics and their supporting details in the road map:

- What technological advancements does each text discuss?
- How do these advancements benefit society?
- What moral dilemma(s) in relation to the advances does each text explore?
- How do members of the scientific community and others featured in the texts respond to this moral dilemma?
- How did their reactions make an impact—on themselves, the people around them, and on society?
- What do the situations described in the texts teach us about the responsibility people must accept when developing new technology intended to benefit mankind?

Use this model to get started with your road map:

INFORMATIVE/EXPLANATORY ESSAY ROAD MAP

THESIS STATEMENT: Society bears a responsibility to ensure that, when developing new technology, it addresses unintended consequences that threaten the sanctity of human life.

Paragraph 1 Main Idea: Pasteur urged his colleagues and students to value human life.
> Supporting Detail #1: Pasteur felt that it was essential that science be aware of its impact on humanity.

> Supporting Detail #2: Pasteur valued life above scientific advancement purely for the sake of advancement.

Paragraph 2 Main Idea: Skloot also sees a conflict between medical advancements and the use of human tissue in research.
> Supporting Detail #1: Henrietta Lack's family was angered by the use of Lack's cells without permission after she died.

> Supporting Detail #2: Though Lack's cells are still used and have helped with essential medical advances, the privacy of her family was once compromised.

Paragraph 3 Main Idea: There can sometimes be conflicting values or controversy regarding scientific experimentation and those affected by it.
> Supporting Detail #1: Pasteur valued his human subjects a great deal and was often anxious and curious about their well-being.

> Supporting Detail #2: Though Henrietta Lacks's cells were essential to much research and discovery, her story had been virtually untold until Skloot took it upon herself to do so.

SKILL: BODY PARAGRAPHS AND TRANSITIONS

 DEFINE

Body paragraphs are the section of the essay between the introduction and conclusion paragraphs. This is where you support your thesis statement by developing your main points with evidence from the text and your own analysis. Typically, each body paragraph will focus on one main point or idea to avoid confusing the reader. The main point of each body paragraph must support the thesis statement.

It is important to structure each of your body paragraphs clearly. One strategy for structuring a body paragraph for an informational essay is the following:

Topic sentence: The topic sentence is the first sentence of your body paragraph and clearly states the main point of the paragraph. It is important that your topic sentence develop the main assertion or central idea you presented in your thesis statement.

Evidence #1: It is important to support your topic sentence with evidence. Evidence can be relevant facts, definitions, concrete details, quotations, or other information and examples derived from the unit texts or sources identified during research.

Analysis/Explanation #1: After presenting evidence to support your topic sentence, you will need to analyze that evidence and explain how it supports your topic sentence and, in effect, your thesis.

Evidence #2: Continue to develop your topic sentence with a second piece of evidence.

Analysis/Explanation #2: Analyze this second piece of evidence and explain how it supports your topic sentence and, in effect, your thesis.

Concluding sentence: After presenting your evidence, you will need to wrap up your main idea and transition to the next paragraph in your concluding sentence.

Transitions are connecting words and phrases that clarify the relationships among ideas in a text. Authors of informative/explanatory texts use transitions to help readers recognize the overall organizational structure of the text. Transitions also help readers make connections among ideas within and across sentences and paragraphs. Also, by adding transition words or phrases to the beginning or end of a paragraph, authors guide readers smoothly through the text.

In addition, transition words and phrases help authors make connections between words within a sentence. Conjunctions such as *and, or,* and *but* and prepositions such as *with, beyond,* and *inside* show the relationships between words. Transitions help readers understand how words fit together to make meaning.

IDENTIFICATION AND APPLICATION

- Body paragraphs are the section of the essay between the introduction and conclusion paragraphs. The body paragraphs provide the evidence and analysis/explanation needed to support the thesis statement. Typically, writers develop one main idea per body paragraph.
    - A topic sentence clearly states the main idea of the paragraph.
    - Evidence consists of relevant facts, definitions, concrete details, quotations, or other information and examples derived from the unit texts or sources obtained from research.
    - Analysis and explanation are needed to explain how the evidence supports the topic sentence.
    - The conclusion sentence wraps up the main point and transitions to the next body paragraph.

- Transition words are a necessary element of a successful piece of informative writing.
    - Transition words help readers understand the text structure of an informative text. Here are some transition words that are frequently used in three different text structures:
    - Cause and effect: *because, accordingly, as a result, therefore, effect, so, for, since*
    - Compare and contrast: *like, unlike, also, both, similarly, although, while, but, however, whereas, conversely, meanwhile, on the contrary, on the other hand, and yet, still*
    - Chronological order: *first, next, then, finally, last, initially, ultimately*

- Transition words help readers understand the flow of ideas and concepts in a text. Some of the most useful transitions are words that indicate that

the ideas in one paragraph are building on or adding to those in another. Examples include: *furthermore, therefore, in addition, moreover, by extension, in order to,* etc.

 MODEL

The Student Model uses a body paragraph structure to develop the main ideas presented in the thesis statement and transitions to help the reader understand the relationship between ideas in the text.

Let's examine the first two body paragraphs from the Student Model essay "The Moral Dilemma of Technology: Benefit versus Harm." Remember to look closely at the structure and note the transition words in bold. Think about the purpose of the information presented. Does each body paragraph effectively develop the main point made in each topic sentence? How do transition words help you to understand the similarities and differences between ideas and experiences in the two texts?

Body Paragraph 1:

> **In 1888,** the Pasteur Institute in Paris—a place where Louis Pasteur and his pupils "could work together for science and the cure of disease"—officially opened (Keim and Lumet 176). **In his address upon its opening,** Pasteur urged his colleagues and students to scrutinize their work and bear moral responsibility for their research, advising them to "Worship the spirit of criticism . . . without it, everything is fallible . . ." **He added that** although science binds itself to no country, a scientist must be aware of "the influence which his works may have in this world." Pasteur felt that awareness applied to science and to its impact on humanity. "Louis Pasteur was a humanist who put himself and science to work to improve the human condition" (Persson 44). **In closing his address,** Pasteur presented his "philosophic reflections" (Keim and Lumet 182) about scientific advancement and making choices between positive and negative impacts of science. "Two contrary laws seem to be wrestling with each other nowadays," Pasteur stated. "[T]he one, a law of blood and death, ever imagining new means of destruction and forcing nations to be constantly ready for the battlefield—the other, a law of peace, work and health, ever evolving new means of delivering man from the scourges which beset him." **For Pasteur,** the choice between the conflicting laws of science—one that "seeks violent conquests" and destruction in war, and the other that finds "relief of humanity" that "places

NOTES

one human life above any victory"—was clear. He would obey "the law of humanity, to extend the frontiers of life."

Note that the first body paragraph of the Student Model is concerned with developing ideas expressed by Louis Pasteur in his address at the opening of the Pasteur Institute in 1888. The paragraph is built on the **topic sentence**, "In his address upon its opening, Pasteur urged his colleagues and students to scrutinize their work and bear moral responsibility for their research . . ." This topic sentence is supported by **evidence,** which includes direct quotations from Pasteur's actual address before the institute. In addition, the writer also quotes Pasteur's biographers and a noted science writer to support the idea that Pasteur was a humanist who believed passionately in taking moral responsibility for the progressive work that scientists do. Toward the end of the paragraph, the writer offers evidence in the form of another quotation from Pasteur's address, one that demonstrates the level of commitment the great scientist believed was necessary when considering the consequences of technological progress in one's work: "'Two contrary laws seem to be wrestling with each other nowadays,' Pasteur stated. '[T]he one, a law of blood and death, ever imagining new means of destruction and forcing nations to be constantly ready for the battlefield—the other, a law of peace, work and health, ever evolving new means of delivering man from the scourges which beset him.'" The paragraph ends with a summary statement that expresses Pasteur's position on the topic.

Notice how the writer carefully integrates several quotations from different types of sources—primary and secondary—to help develop and support the main idea of this paragraph. The writer does not break up the text to indicate the sources from which she is quoting. Rather, she makes quoted material evident through the use of quotation marks, transitional phrases, and source citations. We are introduced to Pasteur's idea of worshipping "the spirit of criticism" as well as the idea of a scientist being aware of "the influence that his work may have in the world" through a quote from his speech. Similarly, we are introduced to the idea of Pasteur's position as a humanist through a cited quotation from a noted science writer—"'Louis Pasteur was a humanist who put himself and science to work to improve the human condition' (Persson 44)"—and to his "philosophical reflections" through his biographers Keim and Lumet.

While the text of the paragraph flows smoothly, as if it was all the creation of the writer, we know exactly when and where the writer is choosing her words and when they are not her own. The flow of ideas is aided by the use of transitions such as "In his address upon its opening," "He added," "In closing his address," and "For Pasteur." The reader is given a sense of how the ideas connect to each other as well as the sequence in which they occurred or were presented.

Now let's examine the second body paragraph of the essay.

Body Paragraph 2:

Pasteur undeniably saw the conflict surrounding technological advancement of his time. He encouraged taking responsibility for research and its consequences. **Rebecca Skloot sees a similar conflict** over advancing medical technology and an "ethical debate surrounding the use of human tissues in research . . ." **In particular,** as Skloot's writing points out, the dilemma she deals with concerns the important medical advancements in the discovery and use of HeLa cells and, in part, the problems medical advances created for the family of Henrietta Lacks, for whom the cells were named. The problems stemmed from the family's anger over the removal of cells from Henrietta's body without permission after she died, over the sale of vials of the cells for $25 for research, and the publication of articles about the cells without their knowledge. Family members felt that the scientific community had taken advantage of them. **In addition,** Henrietta's contribution was not properly acknowledged by the scientific community; indeed, early Internet research conducted by Skloot revealed that most sites referred to her as Helen Lane. **As background,** Skloot tells us that HeLa cells are "said to be 'immortal'" because they were taken from a cancerous tumor that killed Henrietta Lacks and now live on outside her body in culture. **She also says** that billions of HeLa cells are used in laboratories around the world, and that they helped with some of the most important advances in medicine. She further tells us that only after completing some of her own biological research using HeLa cells, Skloot learned through reading magazine articles of the Lacks family's anger. **As a researcher** attempting to discover and tell the whole story of Henrietta Lacks, of HeLa cells, and of technological advances using them, Skloot dug deeper into information about the Lacks family and tried to make sense of the history of cell culture and the ethical debate about human tissue research. Ultimately, she became one voice calling for the scientific community to acknowledge the harm done to the Lacks family as medical advancements were made with HeLa cells. Then, another ethical controversy erupted. German researchers published data from a study of the HeLa genome—the complete genetic material present in a line of HeLa cells. It was "data with the potential to reveal some very private information about Ms. Lacks' descendants, including their risks of various diseases" (Collins).

NOTES

*Many people joined in the demand for moral responsibility. "After outcries from the Lacks family, scientists, bioethicists, and many others, the HeLa genome sequence was removed from a public database" (Collins). **Ultimately, the U.S. National Institutes of Health made amends. An agreement was struck taking into account both the advancement of medical research and the concerns of Lacks' descendants. "In addition, the agreement asks researchers who use or derive genomic data from HeLa cells to acknowledge the contribution of Ms. Lacks and her family in their publications" (Collins).*

In the second body paragraph, the writer turns her attention to ideas from *The Immortal Life of Henrietta Lacks* by Rebecca Skloot. Notice that the writer's use of transitional words and phrases, such as "Rebecca Skloot sees a similar conflict" and "on the other hand," help the reader understand that the overall text structure of the essay is comparison and contrast—that is, the essay explores ways in which the ideas and experiences presented in the two texts are similar and different. These transitional words and phrases also help readers identify specific bases upon which the two texts address similar or different ideas.

PRACTICE

Write one body paragraph for your informative essay that follows the suggested format. When you are finished, trade with a partner and offer each other feedback. How effective is the topic sentence at stating the main point of the paragraph? How strong is the evidence used to support the topic sentence? Are all quotes and paraphrased evidence cited properly? Did the analysis thoroughly support the topic sentence? How effectively are transitions used to clarify the relationships among the ideas in the text? Offer each other suggestions, and remember that they are most helpful when they are constructive.

DRAFT

CA-CCSS: CA.RL.9-10.1, CA.W.9-10.2a, CA.W.9-10.2b, CA.W.9-10.2c, CA.W.9-10.2d, CA.W.9-10.2e, CA.W.9-10.2f, CA.W.9-10.4, CA.W.9-10.5, CA.W.9-10.6, CA.W.9-10.7, CA.W.9-10.8, CA.W.9-10.9a, CA.W.9-10.9b, CA.W.9-10.10, CA.SL.9-10.1a, CA.L.9-10.1b, CA.L.9-10.6

WRITING PROMPT

Mankind has always sought to advance its knowledge of the world and to make life easier and better for its citizens. However, some scientific breakthroughs have led to unintended consequences. Consider both the positive and the negative outcomes that may result from new technology. Recall the selections you have read in this unit and how they explore moral dilemmas posed by technological advancements or possibilities. Choose two selections from the unit and write an informative essay that answers this question: What responsibility do people have when developing new technology? Along with information from the unit selections, include research from at least three other credible print and/or digital sources to support your ideas.

Your essay should include:
- an introduction with a clear thesis statement
- body paragraphs with relevant evidence and thorough analysis to support your thesis
- cited research from at least three credible print and digital sources to support your ideas
- a concluding paragraph that effectively wraps up the essay and summarizes/paraphrases support for the thesis statement

You have already made progress toward writing your own informative/explanatory text. You have thought about the topic and chosen your texts. You have identified what you want to say about the responsibility people have when developing new technology. You have decided how to organize information and gathered supporting details. Now it's time to write a draft.

NOTES

In addition to reading texts that feature major technological advances, you have been studying techniques authors use to convey information. Now you will use those informational writing techniques to compose your own informative essay about the responsibility that accompanies new technology.

As you prepare to write your draft, gather all of your prewriting and planning information, including outlines, organizers, and any other information you feel is essential to begin the process. Keep in mind all of the skills you have learned up to this point: how your audience and purpose inform your writing style; how to research outside sources and take relevant, detailed, useful notes; how to craft a clear and purposeful thesis statement; how to organize your research as well as your thoughts in order to conceptualize your overall intent and purpose for writing; how to plan where to put the information you have gathered according to the outline of an informative/explanatory essay; how to use supporting details to bolster the main ideas of your body paragraphs; how to write an effective introduction to engage the reader and frame the purpose of your essay as well as an impactful conclusion to summarize your points, restate your thesis, and soundly bring your essay to a close; and how to use engaging and smooth transitions throughout your essay to connect all of the ideas and subtopics that support your thesis.

Remember that your draft is not the final essay. While you should maintain an essay format in keeping with informational/explanatory writing, you can use this Draft stage to experiment with different ideas you might have regarding the positive and negative impacts of technology. Remember: you can always remove or delete an idea, but an idea unrecorded is gone forever.

When drafting, ask yourself these questions:

- What can I do to engage my reader? How can I improve my hook to make it more appealing?

- Does my essay follow the suggested format of an introduction, body paragraphs, and a conclusion? Do the ideas and information I have included flow logically?

- Is my thesis statement part of my introduction? Have I presented my thesis statement clearly? What can I do to clarify my thesis statement?

- In each body paragraph, which relevant facts, strong details, and interesting quotations derived from the unit texts and outside research support the thesis statement? Are the main ideas of each paragraph relevant to my overall purpose for writing?

- Have I included clear transitions to show the connections among ideas?

- Would more precise language, such as technical or domain-specific words, or different details about the controversy that surrounds technological advancements make the text more exciting and vivid?

- How effectively does the information I obtained from research enhance my analysis of the unit texts?

- How well have I communicated what moral dilemmas the texts explore in the context of new technology? How have I shown my reader that I have considered both the positive and negative consequences of technology?

- Does my conclusion restate my thesis and effectively summarize the main points of my essay?

- With what final thought do I want to leave my readers?

- Have I used adjective clauses correctly?

SOURCES AND CITATIONS
sync•skills
Writing

SKILL:
SOURCES AND
CITATIONS

DEFINE

When writing an informative/explanatory essay, writers cannot simply make up information or rely on their own subjective experiences or opinions. To thoroughly support the treatment and analysis of their topics, writers need to include information from relevant, accurate, and reliable sources and cite, or acknowledge, them properly. Writers should keep track of these sources as they research and plan their work. When it comes time to write, they can use this information to acknowledge the sources when necessary within the text. If they don't, writers can be accused of **plagiarism,** or stealing someone else's words and ideas. In some academic texts, writers may be asked to provide sources and citations in **footnotes** or **endnotes,** which link specific references within the essay to the correlating pages or chapters in an outside source. In addition to internal citations, writers may also need to provide a full list of sources in a **Works Cited** section or standard **bibliography.**

IDENTIFICATION AND APPLICATION

- As writers research, they consult a variety of sources. Sources can be primary or secondary. Sources also come in a variety of media: print sources, like books and magazines; electronic resources, like internet articles or podcasts; audio-visual sources, such as photographs and films; and living sources, such as anyone you may interview yourself.

- Primary sources are first-hand accounts, artifacts, or other original materials. Examples of primary sources include:

  › letters or other correspondence
  › photographs
  › official documents
  › diaries or journals
  › autobiographies or memoirs
  › eyewitness accounts and interviews
  › audio recordings and radio broadcasts

NOTES

> works of art
> literature, including novels, short stories, poems, and dramas.
> artifacts, or objects

- Secondary sources are usually text. Secondary sources are the written interpretation and analysis of primary source materials. Some examples of secondary sources include:
  > encyclopedia articles
  > textbooks
  > commentary or criticisms
  > histories
  > documentary films
  > news analyses

- Whether sources are primary or secondary, they must be authoritative, which means they are credible and accurate.

- When gathering sources and information for an informative/explanatory text, writers should take note of as much of the following information as possible:
  > Title of the work or website
  > Author(s) or editor(s) of the work
  > Pages referenced, if available (relate this to specific quotations or information)
  > Date of publication
  > Publisher name and address (city, state, and/or country)
  > Medium of publication (web or print)
  > Version numbers (revisions, issue numbers, volumes, editions)
  > Date of access

- Always avoid plagiarism by either quoting the original text directly or paraphrasing the original and crediting the author.

- Different organizations and references, such as the Modern Language Association (MLA), the American Psychological Association (APA), and the *Chicago Manual of Style,* recommend different ways of handling the proper formatting of citations and sources. When you receive an assignment, always check for and follow the proper formatting requirements.

 MODEL

Modern Language Association (MLA) guidelines for citing research sources is the style mostly used in English classes. For detailed guidelines, refer to the *MLA Handbook for Writers of Research Papers* or a reliable online source such as the Purdue Online Writing Lab (OWL).

NOTES

MLA style for citing sources takes a two-pronged approach. Writers following MLA style provide both a Works Cited page and in-text citations. The Works Cited page appears at the end of the essay and lists all the sources cited in the paper. The in-text citations, which appear at the end of sentences that contain researched information, link to the entries on the Works Cited page. These citations often contain **signal words.** Signal words correspond to the first word or first few words of the related entry on the Works Cited page and are typically the author's last name or the first few words of the title.

These are the rules for in-text citations:

- After a quotation or a paraphrase of researched information, insert in parentheses the author's last name and the page number where the information was found. For instance:

  › Without such knowledge, it would remain a "vacant wilderness," as one of Bradford's fellow Pilgrims later called it (Clap, 3).

- If you mention the author's name in the sentence, you do not need to use a signal word in the parentheses:

  › Without such knowledge, it would remain a "vacant wilderness," as Roger Clap, one of Bradford's fellow Pilgrims, later called it in his memoir (3).

- If the source does not indicate the author, use the first few words of the title or if it is short title, the entire title to identify the piece:

  › Without such knowledge, it would remain a "vacant wilderness," as one of Bradford's fellow Pilgrims later called it ("Surviving the First Year" 3).

For the Works Cited page, follow these general formatting guidelines:

- The title Works Cited should be centered at the top of the page and appear in regular font. (It should not be bold or underlined, nor should it be in a font larger than that of the surrounding text.)
- Arrange the entries alphabetically by author's last name or by the first word in the title, if no author is mentioned.
- Long entries, that is, entries that take up more than one line, should be indented half an inch every line after the first.
- The entire list should be double spaced. Some writers mistakenly use single spacing for long entries and then use double spacing between entries. That is not correct. Double spacing should be used between all lines of text.

The format for each entry in the Works Cited list depends on the type of source. Here are two of the most commonly used formats:

Book

Structure:

Last, First M., and First M. Last (for additional author or editor). *Book Title*. City,

State: Publisher, Year Published. Medium.

Example:

Bradford, William, and Harold Paget. *Of Plymouth Plantation*. Mineola, NY:

Dover Publications, 2006. Print.

Website

Structure:

Last, First M. "Article or Page Title." *Website Title*. Website Publisher. Date

Month Year Published (if available). Web. Date Month Year Accessed.

Example:

Clap, Roger. "Surviving the First Year of the Massachusetts Bay Colony,

1630–1631." *American Beginnings*. National Humanities Center, n.d. Web.

21 July 2014.

The Purdue OWL site can serve as a quick reference for examples of many different types of formats, including <u>books, periodicals, electronic sources,</u> and <u>other common sources.</u>

Note that it is common practice to present the titles of full-length works such as books, plays, and movies in italics. Shorter works, such as titles of articles, chapters, short stories, poems, and songs, are presented within quotation marks.

Let's examine how, in this excerpt from the Student Model essay, the writer includes accurate parenthetical citations from both primary and secondary material in the body of her essay:

> *In 1888, the Pasteur Institute in Paris—a place where Louis Pasteur and his pupils "could work together for science and the cure of disease"—officially opened (**Keim and Lumet 176**). In his address upon its opening, Pasteur urged his colleagues and students to scrutinize their work and bear moral responsibility for their research, advising them to "Worship the spirit of criticism . . .without it, everything is fallible . . ." He added that although science binds itself to no country, a scientist must be aware of "the influence*

which his works may have in this world." *Pasteur felt that awareness applied to science and to its impact on humanity. "Louis Pasteur was a humanist who put himself and science to work to improve the human condition" (Persson 44). In closing his address, Pasteur presented his "philosophic reflections" (Keim and Lumet 182) about scientific advancement and making choices between positive and negative impacts of science. "Two contrary laws seem to be wrestling with each other nowadays," Pasteur stated. "[T]he one, a law of blood and death, ever imagining new means of destruction and forcing nations to be constantly ready for the battlefield—the other, a law of peace, work and health, ever evolving new means of delivering man from the scourges which beset him." For Pasteur, the choice between the conflicting laws of science—one that "seeks violent conquests" and destruction in war, and the other that finds "relief of humanity" that "places one human life above any victory"—was clear. He would obey "the law of humanity, to extend the frontiers of life."*

Notice that the first sentence of the paragraph begins with the writer's own words. She discusses factual information about what happened at the opening of the Pasteur Institute in 1888. Within the sentence, the writer describes a goal of the Institute in a clause that is set off by dashes. Within that clause, the writer directly quotes a secondary source. Since these words are not the writer's own but rather the exact words of another author, they are placed in quotation marks. The source of the quote is indicated at the end of the sentence in a citation: "(Keim and Lumet 176)." An internal text citation to "Keim and Lumet" refers to a work by these two authors that is presented in the Works Cited list, which appears at the end of the paper. The number 176 is the page number on which this quotation can be found.

In the Works Cited list at the end of the essay, the writer has provided all of the essential information about works she used in the research and preparation of her essay, in the proper format:

Works Cited

Collins, Francis. "HeLa Cells: A New Chapter in An Enduring Story." *National*

Institutes of Health. U.S. Department of Health and Human Services.

7 August 2013. Web. 12 August 2015.

Dhoke, Ruchira. "LOUIS PASTEUR: the man who built the foundation for the science of microbiology and modern medicine." *The National.* 20 October 2014. Web. 12 August 2015.

Keim, Albert, and Louis Lumet. *Louis Pasteur.* Trans. Frederic Taber Cooper. New York: Frederick A. Stokes, 1914. Print.

Pasteur, Louis. "Worship the Spirit of Criticism." *StudySync.* BookheadEd Learning, LLC., 2015. Web. 12 August 2015.

Persson, Sheryl. *Smallpox, Syphilis, and Salvation: Medical Breakthroughs that Changed the World.* Australia: Exisle Publishing, 2010. Print.

Skloot, Rebecca. *The Immortal Life of Henrietta Lacks.* StudySync. BookheadEd Learning, LLC., 2015. Web. 12 August 2015.

 PRACTICE

Check your in-text citations for quoted information to confirm that they are accurate. Then, using the format in the Student Model, write Works Cited entries for the two unit texts to which you refer in your essay. When you are finished, trade with a partner and offer each other feedback. How successful was the writer in citing sources for the essay on the Works Cited page? Offer each other suggestions, and remember that they are most helpful when they are constructive.

REVISE

CA-CCSS: CA.RI.9-10.1, CA.RI.9-10.2, CA.RI.9-10.3, CA.W.9-10.2a, CA.W.9-10.2b, CA.W.9-10.2c, CA.W.9-10.2d, CA.W.9-10.2e, CA.W.9-10.2f, CA.W.9-10.4, CA.W.9-10.5, CA.W.9-10.6, CA.W.9-10.8, CA.W.9-10.9a, CA.W.9-10.9b, CA.W.9-10.10, CA.SL.9-10.1c, CA.L.9-10.3a

WRITING PROMPT

Mankind has always sought to advance its knowledge of the world and to make life easier and better for its citizens. However, some scientific breakthroughs have led to unintended consequences. Consider both the positive and the negative outcomes that may result from new technology. Recall the selections you have read in this unit and how they explore moral dilemmas posed by technological advancements or possibilities. Choose two selections from the unit and write an informative essay that answers this question: What responsibility do people have when developing new technology? Along with information from the unit selections, include research from at least three other credible print and/or digital sources to support your ideas.

Your informative essay should include:
- an introduction with a clear thesis statement
- body paragraphs with relevant evidence and thorough analysis to support your thesis
- cited research from at least three credible print and digital sources to support your ideas
- a concluding paragraph that effectively wraps up the essay and summarizes/paraphrases support for the thesis statement

You have written a draft of your informative/explanatory text. You have also received input from your peers about how to improve it. Now you are going to revise your draft.

Here are some recommendations to help you revise:
- Review the suggestions made by your peers.
- Focus on maintaining a formal style. A formal style suits your purpose—that is, giving information about a serious topic. It also fits your audience—that

NOTES

is, students, teachers, and other readers interested in learning more about your topic.

› As you revise, eliminate any slang.

› Look for imprecise language. Can you substitute a more precise word, such as a technical or domain-specific word, for a word that is general or dull?

› Remove any first-person pronouns such as "I," "me," or "mine" or instances of addressing readers as "you." These are more suitable to a writing style that is informal, personal, and conversational. Check that you have used all pronouns correctly.

› If you have included your personal opinions, remove them. Your essay should be objective and unbiased.

- After you have revised elements of style, think about whether there is anything else you can do to improve your essay's information or organization.

› Do you need to add any new textual evidence to fully support your thesis statement or engage the interest of readers? For example, is there a detail about someone's moral struggle that a reader might find compelling?

› Did one of your subjects say something special that you forgot to quote? Quotations can add life to your essay. Be sure to cite your sources properly.

› Consider your organization. Would your essay flow better if you strengthened the transitions between paragraphs?

- Double check all your citations and your Works Cited list.

› Have you cited all direct quotations and paraphrased ideas within the body of the essay?

› Is every source you cited in the body of your essay included in your Works Cited list?

› Is there a source on your Works Cited list that you did not include in the essay? Delete that source from the list.

› Are your internal citations and Works Cited list formatted appropriately?

- As you add new details or change information, check your grammar and punctuation.

› Check that you have utilized parallel structure in sentences that include a series.

› Be sure to use semicolons and colons correctly.

› Check that you have used the active voice consistently.

› Check carefully for misspelled words.

NOTES

EDIT, PROOFREAD, AND PUBLISH

CA-CCSS: CA.RI.9-10.1, CA.W.9-10.2a, CA.W.9-10.2b, CA.W.9-10.2c, CA.W.9-10.2d, CA.W.9-10.2e, CA.W.9-10.2f, CA.W.9-10.4, CA.W.9-10.5, CA.W.9-10.6, CA.W.9-10.7, CA.W.9-10.8, CA.W.9-10.9a, CA.W.9-10.9b, CA.W.9-10.10, CA.SL.9-10.1a, CA.SL.9-10.1c, CA.SL.9-10.4a, CA.SL.9-10.6, CA.L.9-10.1a, CA.L.9-10.1b, CA.L.9-10.2c, CA.L.9-10.3a

WRITING PROMPT

Mankind has always sought to advance its knowledge of the world and to make life easier and better for its citizens. However, some scientific breakthroughs have led to unintended consequences. Consider both the positive and the negative outcomes that may result from new technology. Recall the selections you have read in this unit and how they explore moral dilemmas posed by technological advancements or possibilities. Choose two selections from the unit and write an informative essay that answers this question: What responsibility do people have when developing new technology? Along with information from the unit selections, include research from at least three other credible print and/ or digital sources to support your ideas.

Your informative essay should include:
- an introduction with a clear thesis statement
- body paragraphs with relevant evidence and thorough analysis to support your thesis
- cited research from at least three credible print and digital sources to support your ideas
- a concluding paragraph that effectively wraps up the essay and summarizes/paraphrases support for the thesis statement

You have revised your informative/explanatory essay and received input from your peers on that revision. Now it is time to edit and proofread your essay to produce a final version.

As you edit your final version, ask yourself the following questions:
- Does my essay follow the basic structure of an informative/explanatory essay? (introduction, body paragraphs, conclusion)

- Does my introduction grab readers' attention in an interesting yet relevant way? Is my thesis statement part of my introduction as well as my conclusion? Does it respond to the prompt clearly and effectively?

- Have I included strong main ideas, supporting details, and relevant evidence from unit texts as well as outside research sources to support my thesis and create a cohesive, vivid presentation of what I want to say?

- Have all of my sources been cited properly both within the body of my essay and in my Works Cited list? Are all of my research sources appropriate (credible, comprised of both primary and secondary, NOT Wikipedia, etc.)?

- Do I use appropriate and smooth transitions to connect ideas and details within paragraphs as well as between paragraphs?

- Have I presented my readers with a conclusion that summarizes my purpose and intent, coherently restates my thesis, and wraps up my essay effectively?

- Have I established and maintained a formal style and objective tone?

- Have I replaced dull or imprecise words with more interesting and precise ones?

- Have I incorporated all the valuable suggestions from my peers?

When you are satisfied with your work, move on to proofread it for errors. For example, check that you have used correct punctuation for quotations, citations, and restrictive/nonrestrictive phrases and clauses. Have you used pronouns correctly? Have you corrected any misspelled words?

- Check that you have formatted your essay according to approved guidelines and standards. This includes proper headings, title placement, margins, font, spacing, essay structure, and bibliographic information, as well as any other technical considerations that come to mind. For example, articles, speeches, and poem titles should be regular font, Title Case, with quotation marks; excerpts from books or novels should be Title Case in italics.

- Check sentence structure, including use of compound sentences and parallel structure.

- Check that you have used adjective clauses correctly.

- Check that you have used active voice and passive voice appropriately.

- Check your use of sentence punctuation, confirming the appropriate use of commas, semicolons, colons, periods, and any other punctuation. Check carefully for punctuation that might be missing or misplaced.

- Check the content and punctuation of quotations and citations.

- Check that each in-text citation matches a complete reference in your Works Cited list.

- Check your spelling, paying special attention to the names of authors, titles, and individuals described in the texts.

Once you have made all your corrections, you are ready to publish your work. You can distribute your writing to family and friends, hang it on a bulletin board, or post it on your blog. If you publish online, create links to your sources and citations. That way, readers can follow-up on what they have learned from your essay and read more on their own.

Text Fulfillment Through StudySync

If you are interested in specific titles, please fill out the fo
below and we will check availability through our partne

ORDER DETAILS

Date:

TITLE	AUTHOR	Paperback/ Hardcover	Specific Edition *If Applicable*	Quantit

SHIPPING INFORMATION

Contact:

Title:

School/District:

Address Line 1:

Address Line 2:

Zip or Postal Code:

Phone:

Mobile:

Email:

BILLING INFORMATION   *SAME AS SHIPPING*

Contact:

Title:

School/District:

Address Line 1:

Address Line 2:

Zip or Postal Code:

Phone:

Mobile:

Email:

PAYMENT INFORMATION

☐ CREDIT CARD   Name on Card:

Card Number: Expiration Date: Security Code:

☐ PO   Purchase Order Number:

StudySync Text Fulfillment, BookheadEd Learning, LLC
610 Daniel Young Drive | Sonoma, CA 95476